Raising a Riot

ALFRED TOOMBS

Raising a Riot

Illustrated by Dorothy McKay

PEOPLES BOOK CLUB · CHICAGO

To CONNIE, without whom . . .

Raising a Riot

THE cottage had been closed for the winter, and when I opened the door that day I was confronted with the sort of wild disorder that is normal in a boy's closet. First, it was necessary to blaze a series of trails through the house, to indicate the routes around the packing cases, piles of furniture, and mountains of dust. Then I tried to decide what should be done first. It was late in the afternoon and dinner had to be cooked, dishes washed, beds made, and floors swept—immediately. Finally the realization came that there was no one to do any of these things but me.

Deciding to start cooking dinner first, I put some potatoes on to boil and washed the green beans. As I was looking for a pot big enough to hold all the beans, one of the children told me that the puppy had just run off with the package of hamburger. Doggedly I shut off the fire under the potatoes and poured the water into the glass coffee maker my mother had pressed on me. She had assured me that even I couldn't go wrong with it. Just then, my son Larry called:

"Daddy?"

"What is it?" I asked.

"When do we eat?"

Before I could give a snappy answer, the coffee maker erupted like Old Faithful, showering the ceiling and walls with a light brown liquid. The bakery lemon meringue pie which I had set near the stove was riddled and completely deflated by a broadside of coffee grounds. Luckily, there was a wall near me; I leaned against it for support and, in a desperate sort of way, began to wonder how I had got myself into this. The events of the last few days flashed before me suddenly. . . .

I had arrived in New York the week before, back home after three years of the war in Europe, to find my wife *hors de combat* —packed off on doctor's orders for a complete change and a therapy that might go on for years. My harassed mother had been minding our three children until my return and she was beginning to look like a candidate for a rest cure herself. She had suggested that we all move to Washington to live with her, but I had declined the invitation.

"You'll have to get a housekeeper if you stay here," she said sternly.

"I'm not going to stay here," I said. "I don't like this city life— all this pushing and shoving and heat and noise."

"What are you going to do, then?"

"Me for the country," I said gaily. "If you and Dad will let me, I'd like to go down to the island for the summer."

The "island" is a summer cottage which my family owns in southern Maryland. My father loves the place. But because of its remoteness and the hazards it presents to the sensible housekeeper, my mother will have none of it. So she fixed me now with an icy stare.

"Bad as things are," she said, "you have to think of something worse. What will you do for a living in the country?"

"I want to go back to writing."

"And who can you get down there to cook, clean house, and watch over these three wild Indians?" she asked.

"Why," I said casually, "I'll do it myself, of course. I'll just have to get them organized—something women don't understand. Then everything will take care of itself."

I still remember the strange way she looked at me—for such a *long* time.

The children's reactions to the plan were somewhat mixed. Larry, who was ten years old, was not enchanted with the prospect of getting so far away from Forty-Second Street and Broadway. He could not picture himself leading The Full Life without a movie house and a corner drugstore nearby. He winced at the prospect of waiting a couple of days longer for the appearance of his favorite blood-and-thunder comic book.

The girls were more composed. Lynn, who was seven years old, seemed quite willing to take her chances anywhere with Daddy, even in the wilds of Maryland. Our youngest, Leslie Eugenie—whose name, for understandable reasons, has been shortened to Janie—was only four years old. At that age, it is difficult to visualize the difference between a few hours and a few months out of the future, and so this radical move seemed to her to be as routine as a week-end visit.

In an effort to overcome any lingering doubts the children might have, I said: "We'll get a dog!"

Larry brightened up immediately.

"Oh, boy!" he said.

"And a cat, too?" Lynn asked.

"An' uh cat for me, too?" asked Janie.

"Cats later on," I said. "We'll start with a dog."

[3]

That night I telephoned my father to tell him of the plan. We all fell to in a frenzy of packing and two days later were ready to leave New York. As I piled up the baggage, Larry looked at everything with a deep suspicion.

"Where's the dog?" he demanded.

"What am I—Clyde Beatty or something? I've got enough wild animals on my hands now. We'll get the dog later."

Somewhat reluctantly he agreed to leave town with nothing more tangible than this assurance.

Somehow we weathered the trip reasonably well. And when we arrived in Washington, we taxied to my family's home, where I planned to take on water and provisions before pushing into the wilds of southern Maryland.

It was agreed that I would buy enough food to last us for the rest of the week. The country stores stocked almost nothing in the way of fresh meat or produce, and my mother promised that she would buy some food for us each week and send it down with my father, who always spent his week ends at the place.

Until I set out for the super-market that day, my shopping experience had been limited to the purchase of an occasional loaf of pumpernickel or the sort of cheese that no one in the family would eat except me. But now I found myself in a jungle of boxes, cans, bottles, steaks, and bolognas. I knew immediately that I was in trouble. Not only was I ignorant of what to buy, but also of how much—and I didn't know how to cook anything, anyway.

The children began to stack up my shopping cart with cereal —choosing only the kind with their favorite comic characters on the box—and quantities of peanut butter, cookies, jam, potato chips, and fruit juice. In the process, Janie upset one of those pyramids of eggs, and so I found myself buying three dozen eggs, more or less damaged. The only things I could find at the meat counter that I could cook were hot dogs and hamburger.

Then I started to wonder where the vitamins were coming from, so I wandered over to the vegetable department and began to fill a sack with spinach. But although I put as much in the sack as I thought we could eat, it weighed just half a pound, and I began to wonder. Turning to a lady shopper, I asked how much spinach it took to feed four or five people.

"You'd better get a bigger bag," she said. "It'll take two or three times as much as you have there."

"That looks like a lot," I said to her, when I had filled a big bag.

"It shrinks," she explained.

My eyes falling on green beans next, I got another bag the same size and started to work filling it. By now the helpful lady had moved on, so I couldn't ask her, when I had filled the sack, whether five pounds of green beans was too much. I guessed they would probably shrink too, with the strings taken off. Finally we had everything and I staggered to the counter with my burden. The clerk whistled happily and the cash register began to whirl with a fury that made the store manager rub his hands with satisfaction.

"That'll be $18.75," said the clerk.

My father was ready to drive us down to the country by the time we were back from the store. We packed the car, and the girls hopped in happily; but Larry stood firm.

"Where's the dog?" he demanded.

"Oh, brother," I exclaimed. "He wants to get a dog in *here!*"

"You promised us we could have a dog," he insisted, getting belligerent now.

"Sure, but I didn't say we'd get it today."

"I want a dog," he insisted. "Now."

"Get in the car. If we pass a kennel on the way, maybe we'll stop and look at some."

It started to rain just after we crossed the city limits. It was one of those midsummer cloudbursts and I could hardly see the road ahead as we crept along. After a time, out of the back seat where children, suitcases, and groceries were struggling desperately for *lebensraum,* came a small, insistent voice.

"Daddy?"

"What is it, Larry?"

"I just saw a sign that said there's a kennel—one mile ahead."

"In this rain, you want to stop and look at dogs?"

"You promised . . ."

This, I told myself, could get serious. Mustn't let the kids down, the very first thing. So when I saw the sign pointing to the kennel, I swerved into the driveway. I figured we might look at a few dogs that day, without actually buying one. But the children fell in love with every animal in the place and within a few minutes I was trying anxiously to hold them down to only *one* dog. We finally agreed upon a fat, floppy-eared female Beagle hound and resumed our journey. The children had packed her in near the groceries and she was soon joyfully burrowing into the box in search of meat. As the afternoon wore on, the rain stopped, and by the time we reached the cottage, all that remained of the deluge was a few puddles on the ground.

Getting out of the car I took a deep breath and paused for a minute to look around. It was here that I had spent my sum-

[6]

mers as a boy and, at the moment, it looked as beautiful as I remembered it. Across the Potomac River, five miles away, I could see the long clay promontory, the Nomini Cliffs, rising from the water's edge. Down the river a short distance was Blakiston Island. The two ships bearing the colonists who settled Maryland under Calvert paused here early in the 1600's to celebrate their first Mass in America.

The river water sparkled in the late afternoon sun and the shadows had begun to lengthen across Dukehart Creek, which runs around, behind, and beside our place. At high tide, the river and the creek join across the neck of land connecting our property to the mainland—and so we call it "the island." I looked at the small white cottage for a moment before entering. It was a place which my father had largely built and rebuilt himself, on week ends and vacations. Well, this is home, I told myself, and opened the door.

The sound of Larry's voice brought me out of my trance.
"Daddy?"
"Yes," I said.
"What's the matter?"
"Oh, nothing, I was just thinking."
"Gee, you looked so funny I thought you were sick."
I began to clean up the coffee grounds and then turned to see what I could salvage of the lemon pie.
At this moment my father appeared in the door of the kitchen and asked:
"How soon will dinner be ready?"
"I don't know," I replied, a little irritably.
"I'm going up on the roof to patch a leaky place," he said.
After sending Larry out to watch Dad work, I tried to get on

with my cooking. I had just begun to make fast motions when I heard Janie's voice.

"Daddy?"

"Yes?"

"Button my dolly's dress, will you?"

"Can't. I'm washing dishes."

"Gran'mommy allas does it for me."

"Okay. Okay. Bring your dolly here."

"Daddy?" said Lynn.

"Yes?"

"The dog's made a puddle in here."

When I had cleaned up the puddle, I called the children together and said firmly:

"Look, every time any of you ask me a question, I have to answer you twice. First you say: 'Daddy?' and I have to say 'What?' Then you ask me whatever question you had on your mind in the first place and I have to give you another answer. Now can't we do away with this 'Daddy' routine? Just ask your questions right out."

Everyone nodded, as if each understood, and I turned around to go back to work.

"Daddy?" said Larry.

"Yes," I answered automatically.

"When do we eat?"

Probably I would have gone into that whole thing about "Daddy" all over again, but suddenly the beans boiled over. They weren't shrinking, as I had expected, and I began to suspect that five pounds of green beans were more than we needed for one meal. I mashed the potatoes and then suddenly remembered that I had meant to cook some hot dogs. I turned off the fire under the beans, and, by the time I had cooked the meat, both vegetables had grown cold. But I was so elated with my culinary achievements that a detail of this kind couldn't dismay me. My announcement that dinner was ready produced no response. So I yelled again. Then I went out to try to find the customers.

After five or ten minutes, I located the children. They were paddling around the creek, in hot pursuit of a crab. When I got them ashore, I climbed the roof and located my father there. He was lightly coated with roofing tar.

"It'll take me a while to clean up for supper," he said sadly. "You should have let me know a little sooner."

Valiantly I took a deep breath and counted to ten. Then I heard Lynn's voice summoning me from below.

"Daddy?"

"Yes?"

"You better come down. The puppy just stole one of the hot dogs."

As I started down the ladder, I said to myself:

"Mother warned me there'd be days like this. But they can't *all* be this way—or can they?"

Chapter Two

DAWN came early the next morning—earlier than I can ever remember.

During the war, I had learned to sleep through air raids and shell fire, but I found that three children getting up in the morning make much more noise. Mine came out of bed swinging and yelling. The minute I opened my eyes, I had an awful feeling that I was behind with my work—and I lay there for a few seconds, counting the days until the week end. My mother had promised to visit us then, and I was anticipating a couple of days of blessed relief.

Now I staggered into the bathroom and prepared to shave as usual. Then it occurred to me that I had better put the coffee on first. The children were already clamoring for breakfast and it seemed advisable to forego my shave, for the time being. But, I took the precaution of locking the outside doors while I cooked the meal, so I'd be sure to find all my customers on deck when it was ready.

Things went along peacefully until the moment when, having scrambled the eggs to the point of near perfection, I took a small step back from the stove to admire my creation. Then I heard

[11]

a crunch, followed by a sharp yip, and looked down to see that I had stepped on the puppy's paw. The children deserted their cereal bowls and rushed to the spot. The kitchen, which a moment before had been a quiet place where a man was cooking a few eggs, was suddenly filled with sound and fury. I got down on my knees to comfort the dog, and then, of course, the eggs burned.

At this moment, I let out a wail loud enough to be heard above all else. The children, who had been mourning loudly over the puppy, broke it off sharply on high C and looked at me with their mouths open. Even the dog stopped yipping. Home had never, never been like this.

Before they could recover sufficiently to start making more noise, I herded the children back to the table and began a new batch of eggs. Then, with breakfast out of the way, I put the whole outfit out of the house and tried to discover exactly where I stood. As nearly as I could make out, I was immediately behind a very large eight ball. There were breakfast dishes to wash. The house was a mess. It would soon be time for dinner —since we always followed the custom, in southern Maryland, of eating the big meal at midday. I rubbed my chin thoughtfully, trying to decide which to tackle first, and that reminded me that I still needed a shave.

By dashing wildly in all directions at once, I managed to get some housecleaning done before it was time to start cooking dinner. The night before, I had received my first lesson in How Not to Cook. Now I was ready for my second. Apparently the trouble had been that I had tried to cook things one at a time. Today, I would do everything at once. I had managed to recover the hamburger from the puppy before she had torn the package open, and I put this on to cook. At the same time I began to warm up the leftover beans—all four pounds of them. The potatoes I put on a third burner, and by the time everything else was cooked, the potatoes were still raw. So dinner came out exactly the same way again—two thirds cold or overcooked and one third undercooked. Somehow, I managed to coax everyone to eat.

Then I set about the business of the afternoon—hurrying to do the dinner dishes, so I could get back to housecleaning; racing through that so I could keep my promise to take the children swimming; rushing in from the river to clean up the mess the puppy had made.

Dazed and glassy-eyed, I collapsed into a chair later in the afternoon to find myself staring at the face of a clock which warned me that it was time to get supper on the table. It turned out to be a light supper—or, at least, what would have seemed like a light supper in the days when I was simply an eater and not a cook. But by the time the meal was over, I was on the verge of complete exhaustion. The children bounded from the table with their normal jet-assisted take-off, but I barely had the strength to drag myself away.

Still, by dint of long years of practice as a husband, I made the trip from the dinner table to an easy chair. I sank into the chair in a normal after-supper stupor, waiting for someone to clear off the table and wash the dishes. It was a few minutes before the awful realization burst upon me that this time no one was handy to perform this little task for me. I was strictly on my own.

Finally I gathered energy to drag myself out and dunk that stack of dishes which, no matter how thoroughly washed, seemed to reappear as if by magic every few hours, dirtier than ever. When the dishes were done, I made my way unsteadily back to the easy chair—but I had hardly touched bottom when I remembered that there were three children to put to bed.

After a full thirty seconds of relaxation, I got up to supervise the work of peeling off three sets of clothes, washing three faces and six hands, and brushing three sets of teeth. Then I had to hunt for misplaced dolls and stuffed animals, without which the girls would never consider going to sleep. Tinker, the puppy, had to be corralled as a bed mate for Larry. This done, I groped toward the easy chair with the grim determination to put a good, solid dent in its seat.

But I had not been there long before I remembered that nothing had been prepared for tomorrow's dessert. Heaving myself up I fixed some chocolate pudding. This time, vowing that I wouldn't get out of that chair again except in case of fire, I reviewed the situation carefully to make sure there was nothing else that had to be done. Fortunately I couldn't find any more urgent housework to do, but as I settled down the haunting realization came that I had not written a single line that day. I wrestled with my conscience on that score for a few minutes, but then the whole question was settled when I glanced at my watch and found that it was already past the hour when country folk should retire.

By calling upon what seemed to be my final ounce of strength, I was able to get to the bedroom and throw off my clothes. I flattened myself out on the mattress with the relaxed finality of an egg dropped on concrete. In my battered condition, I estimated that it might take as long as three seconds for me to get to sleep. Just then I remembered that I had forgotten to put fruit juice in the refrigerator to chill for breakfast. With all the enthusiasm of a boy setting off for the first day of school, I crept out of bed and into the kitchen. When I got back to bed, the

[14]

horrible thought that I might have forgotten something else gave me insomnia—and it took all of ten seconds for me to get to sleep.

In those first days, I never moved at a pace slower than a dead gallop. From the awful second in the morning when the first child's war whoop awakened me until the time at night when I dropped off to sleep—wondering what to have for dessert the next day—there was never a moment, dull or otherwise, that I could call my own. Housekeeping was certainly the hardest job I had ever tackled. It requires the use of all known muscles— and some which we have not yet developed—plus a considerable amount of intelligence and all of the virtues. Other jobs tax a number, or perhaps all, of these resources, but housekeeping is the only one that's run on the basis of the 140-hour week.

Waking up in the morning is the worst mistake that a housekeeper can make. You have the awful feeling that you are in debt to the day. You have a terrible sense of urgency, a need to hurry because you know that, the minute you open your eyes, you're behind with your work. Housekeeping is like owing money to a loan shark who charges one hundred per cent interest. You work all day to pay off the debt, and the minute you awaken the next day you find that you owe exactly as much as you did the day before.

When I'd get out of bed, bleary-eyed and creaking in every joint, I'd find the children full of more energy than a bucket of atoms. In shrill tones they'd demand that I fix buckwheat cakes for breakfast, and fry a few fish on the side. Then, during that longest ten minutes of the day—while the morning's first cup of coffee is brewing—they'd inflict upon my person all the indignities conceived by the Katzenjammer Kids in twenty-five years of operation. If I lived through this—and I usually did—I

[15]

was free to face the real problems of the day. Somehow, I never caught up with the work. My feet swelled, my hands puffed up, my back ached, and my head spun. But still there was something more to do.

In happier days gone by, I had taken it for granted that the home was managed by invisible hands. Now, I was learning the hard way. My struggle with the girls' hair was typical of the sort of education I was getting. The morning of the first day, they came to me with hairbrushes in hand. Although I had always been an ardent admirer of their golden tresses, I had assumed that their hair fell to their shoulders in a symmetrical way without any particular human assistance.

But it took me thirty minutes to straighten out the snarls, brush out the sand, and find all the cockle burrs that morning. And by mid-afternoon, they both looked as if they'd been in a hurricane and I had to go through the whole process all over again. After a few days of this, I thought seriously of shaving the two girls bald.

The only thing that kept me alive through that first week was the realization that my mother would be down on the week end. I began to have visions—like the mirages seen by stragglers in the desert—of sleeping late on Saturday morning, of sitting down to eat a dinner that someone else had cooked, of seeing dishes cleared off the table and washed by other hands, of children being whisked off to bed without my having to do anything about it but kiss them good night.

Since my mother and father were to arrive on Friday night, toward the end of the week I began to gather new strength. My venture into housekeeping had become a controversial subject among all those who had heard of it. And most of my friends confidently predicted that within a short time the children would be suffering from acute indigestion, ptomaine poisoning, or pellagra and that the house would become so filled with debris that it would be necessary to send a rescue party in to dig us out. Because of these predictions, I went to particular pains, before the week end, to make sure that both the children and the cottage were as clean as a parson's mind. Then I sat back to await praise and a brief respite.

When my parents arrived on the great evening, Mother looked the children over carefully and, having counted fingers and toes to make sure none was missing, peeked under the rug to see if that was where I had swept the dust. I related the adventures of the week, dwelling at some length on my physical complaints, the quality of the groceries available locally, and the way the children were outgrowing their clothes. My mother listened to all this with a superior sort of smile and a distant look in her eyes. She made no comment until I told her how much I had spent on groceries.

"Humph," she said, "you'll be in the poorhouse in a month at that rate. Why don't you make out a budget?"

This, I suppose, should have given me some indication of how things had changed. Mother and I talked on and on for the rest of the evening about housekeeping. My father could arouse no interest at all in the latest political scandal, and he finally gave me up as a conversational loss.

Next morning, when the kids began their dance to greet the dawn, I merely rolled over and tried to go back to sleep, in the hope that Mother would get up and do something about them. But she didn't move a muscle for a long time. Finally, she poked her head in the bedroom door.

"What time do the children have breakfast?" she asked.

"Oh, whenever we get up," I said hopefully.

[17]

"You mean it's like this every morning?" she said reprovingly. "You ought to feed them as soon as *they* get up."

Obediently I climbed out of bed and started to work on breakfast, while Mother lay in her bed talking to the kids. When I put the meal on the table, she showed up, looking rested and cheerful.

"Coffee's a little weak, isn't it?" she said. "Maybe I'd better get up and fix coffee tomorrow."

The look I gave her should have turned weak coffee strong. "Any time," I said. "Any time."

Next she surveyed the toast, with slightly burned edges, and said helpfully:

"I've got an extra toaster in town. Makes wonderful toast. Would you like me to bring it down?"

Mother did volunteer to cook dinner, but she couldn't find any of the things she needed. When I tried to explain that the stuff in the can marked "Sugar" was really salt, that the flour was in a corn-meal bag in the old fireless cooker where mice couldn't reach it, and that she'd have to use a pair of pliers and a monkey wrench to turn on the oven, she threw up her hands in horror and quit.

"I'll do the dishes," she said. "But you'll have to do the cooking."

And so, with her pointing out ever so tactfully how I should be doing it, I cooked the meal. She did the dishes and while she was at it decided to straighten up the kitchen. The result was that when suppertime came, I couldn't find anything. The cinnamon wasn't in the pepper shaker any more, sugar was back in the can marked "Sugar," and every time I reached for a pan that I had kept in a certain place, I'd find that it had been moved.

[18]

"Women certainly do upset things," Larry remarked in disgust.

After that, I decided to paddle my own culinary canoe and we posted a sign on the kitchen door: "No Women Allowed, Except Dishwashers."

Sunday evening, when my parents started back to town, I walked to the car with them. Mother promised that she would be back in a couple of weeks and, while this seemed to be a pleasant enough social occasion to anticipate, I found that I wasn't looking forward to it in quite the same light as before.

My father had accepted the whole atmosphere of health and cleanliness around the house that week end just as naturally as if he had been visiting Emily Post. He had made no comment about any of it up to the time when he started to get in the car. Then I noticed that he was looking at me and frowning.

"Son," he said, "you should be more careful about your personal appearance. I don't think you've shaved for a week."

I felt my face and knew that he couldn't have been more accurate. I thought back to the morning of our first day there and my decision to postpone my shave until after breakfast. Since then, in the course of my eighteen-hour housekeeping days, there just hadn't been an opportunity. I knew then why a far-seeing Providence had given beards to men only.

No housewife could possibly find time to shave.

Chapter Three

ON the second day of our stay in the country, Larry came to the door of the kitchen and asked timidly:

"Is it all right if I go barefooted?"

"Why, of course," I told him.

He was back a few minutes later.

"May I go down to the beach?"

"Sure."

"And wade?"

"Certainly. Do what you like."

He disappeared like a flash to spread the news to his sisters. It took Larry—who was broken to city life, if ever a boy can be—a time to grow accustomed to the lack of confinement that was now his. It seemed to me that the words children hear most often are "No" or "Don't." So, with the enthusiasm of a brand-new parent, I resolved to reserve those admonitions for the most occasional use. I let it be understood that nothing was prohibited, except the sort of activity which endangered others' life, limb, or property.

In this atmosphere, Larry began to expand. It was not the sort of gradual, graceful change that one might expect when a boy is transferred from one environment to another. It was almost explosive in its force—like one of those sun-burst fireworks displays, where a tiny ball of fire suddenly blazes out in all directions in the sky. Feeling no restraints, he began to dash wildly in all directions trying to find some.

However, I weathered these storms with an equanimity which I considered truly saintly, and never once did the forbidden word "Don't" pass my lips. But there are limits to all things mortal, and it was on the day that we made a trip by boat to the Virginia shore that Larry and I found ours. We had a picnic lunch along the shore, at the foot of the towering clay cliffs, and then set out to hunt for shells and shark's teeth. Carelessly I took my eyes off Larry for a few minutes, when I looked for him, I discovered that he and the dog had started to scramble up the face of the bluff. There were gullies, erosions, and ledges for the first seventy-five feet and the two of them covered this distance quickly.

By the time I had spotted my son, he was starting up the almost sheer rise to the top, looking like a little brown spider. I watched him spellbound, deciding whether this was the time to call a halt. But figuring that he was more likely to break his neck if I started yelling, I let him go on. So I stood at the bottom, waiting to pick up the pieces if he lost his footing.

Finally, he pulled himself over the ledge at the top, nearly a hundred and fifty feet above water level. The dog was sitting on a mound of dirt, halfway up, howling mournfully because she could get no higher. I expected that Larry would start down after catching his breath, but instead he started to scramble up a tree at the top of the cliff! Then he began to work his way out on a branch that hung over the cliff. At that point, he had reached my limit.

"Don't do that," I yelled frantically.

He backed off and climbed down the tree. Then I had to watch him work his way down the cliff again, and finally he came running up to us triumphantly.

"Made it," he said breathlessly.

"Yes," I said. "But why? What did you find up there?"

"Nothing," he said.

This, I discovered a couple of days later, was not entirely accurate. Because at the point where he had pulled himself over the top of the cliff he must have found a very large bed of poison ivy. He was covered with the rash from head to toes and I spent most of my time for three or four days bandaging and putting lotion on him. This ended Larry's Era of Utter Freedom.

Larry was a big, noisy, aggressive kid, who roared around the house with all the grace of a stampeding rhinoceros. In reality, he was nothing but a self-propelled appetite, with seemingly insatiable cravings for food, information, and attention. This was no Tom Sawyer, with a pocketful of useless trinkets, a dead rat on a string, and a mind crammed with folksy superstition. This was a new and sinister evolvement of the Genus Boy, exhibiting characteristics which could not possibly be hereditary. He asked questions about the family life of the turtle and wanted to know the distance, in light years, from Mars to Venus. When a relative sent him a book giving the answers to 1001 questions, I looked for a brief respite from the stream of queries addressed to me—but each of the 1001 questions suggested 1001 more for him to ask.

He drank milk out of fourteen-ounce glasses, ate four-decker sandwiches, and consumed spinach by the peck. He said he didn't like eggplant, and when I suggested that he try to learn to like it, he scornfully informed me it was a waste of time—since it was low in vitamin content. He would shine my shoes, if he thought it would get him a pat on the head, or pull his sisters' hair, if he thought it would get him a paddling—any attention, favorable or unfavorable, being preferable to none.

Lynn was the antithesis of her brother—or perhaps, more accurately, the reaction to him. She was dainty, mild, and diplomatic—very diplomatic. One day, when the kids returned from their daily trip to the store, she came sidling up to me in the kitchen. She had a serious look on her face and, obviously, something on her mind.

"Daddy?" she said, since all conversation with me began this way.

"Yes?" I said.

"What are we going to have for dessert?"

"I haven't decided."

"That's good."

"Why?"

"I was wondering if we could have bread pudding."

"I suppose so. If that's what you want."

"Yes. That's what we want."

I attached no particular significance to any of this and went on with my work. But Lynn stayed near me, studying me with her serious eyes.

"Daddy?" she said after a time.

"Yes?"

"Were you planning any special vegetable for dinner?"

"I thought we'd have a salad. You kids got the tomatoes at the store, didn't you?"

"Well, yes. But I was wondering if we could have stewed tomatoes."

"I guess so. Where are the groceries, anyway?"

"They're outside."

"Well, why didn't you bring them in?"

"I was just waiting to make sure we wouldn't have to go back. But if we can have stewed tomatoes and bread pudding, it'll be all right."

By now, it had dawned on me that something was amiss.

"What are you talking about?" I demanded.

"We had a little trouble."

"What sort of trouble?"

"Well, Tinker got in six fights with other dogs."

"And what happened?"

"Finally, she got away from us."

"Yes. But for heaven's sake, what happened?"

"A car was coming along the road."

By now, my hair was standing on end. I had visions of dead dogs, injured children, and wrecked automobiles. I got a good grip on the edge of the table.

"So what happened?"

"Larry tackled the dog."

"Yes?"

"That's when he mashed the tomatoes."

"Is that all?"

"And the bread."

"Did he hurt himself?"

"No."

"Is the dog all right?"

"Yes. But we thought that if you didn't want to have bread pudding and stewed tomatoes, so we could use that mashed stuff, we might have to go back."

I was so relieved to find that everyone was still in one piece

[24]

that I forgot to get upset about my crushed groceries. We ate stewed tomatoes and bread pudding without another word being said on the subject. It wasn't until some days later, when Lynn again came sidling up to me in her hesitant way and started asking questions, that I caught on to the pattern.

"Daddy?" she said.

"Yes?"

"Don't you think Janie's hair needs cutting?"

"Well, I suppose it is getting a little too long. Why?"

"I was wondering whether you'd rather cut it or wash the paint out."

"What paint?"

"That green paint on the shelf in the tool house."

I had just spent an hour of my time working on the girls' hair and, had the news been broken to me in any other way, I might have reacted with a greater show of violence. As it was, I rushed out to find Janie, and when I discovered that nothing worse had happened than the application of a first coat on her scalp, I forgot to get mad. It was hard to get mad at her anyway. She was more like a bear cub than a child, with the sort of sophistication that belongs to some humans at the age of four. When I had washed and cut the paint out of her hair, I gave her a kiss.

"Daddy, you're a wolf," she said.

The questions she brought to me were, perhaps, not as relevant as those raised by her older brother, but certainly they were no less difficult.

"Daddy," she asked, "which do you like better, fairies or angels?"

"I don't know," I said. "It's hard to say."

"But which do you like best?"

"I can't decide. Which do you like?"

"I don't know," she said, then added thoughtfully: "I don't know what angels do."

Janie refused to be taken anything but seriously. Whatever the rest of us did, she had to do also. The first time we went fishing, I rigged up lines for Larry and Lynn, but suggested to Janie that she content herself with helping me to tend mine. This would not do, for she insisted that she must have one of her own. I thought she would drop the line in the water and I'd hear no more of it, but every few minutes she pulled up her line and said:

"I fink I got somefin'."

It turned out regularly that the something she thought she had on her line had departed with her bait. So I gave her some more bait and went back to watching my own line. After a time, I got out of the habit of paying any attention to Janie's announcements until she came to the point where she wanted more bait. But I had badly underestimated her. Because a short moment after she had told us for the fifteenth time that she had something, I heard a loud plop on the bottom of the boat. And when I looked up, Janie was proudly surveying her line, on the end of which was a fish just a little bit smaller than herself.

"Vere," she said, "I fought I had somefin'."

Janie was enthusiastic about life in the country, but I did not understand exactly why until she looked at me earnestly one day and said:

"Daddy, I like it here better 'an New York or Washin'ton."

"That's nice," I replied. "Why do you like it better?"

"Sand," she told me, waving her arm in the direction of the beach. "All 'at sand."

I attributed the chaos marking my first weeks of house-keeping to my lack of familiarity with the field. But when conditions continued to get worse rather than better, I decided that it was time I got things organized—as I had assured my mother I would do. So one day I called the children together and said:

"This is getting to be too much of a job for me. You kids are big enough to help with things around here."

They agreed readily and offers of assistance came from all sides. Larry said he would help out by giving the puppy a bath every week—a chore which he was already performing. Janie volunteered to do the cooking for me. Lynn promised that she would put the cap back on the toothpaste tube whenever she found it missing and also offered to wash the dog. But I had in mind something a little more extensive than this.

"No, we've really got to get organized," I insisted. "We could run this place like an army. I'll be in command. Larry can be the first sergeant. Lynn can be a corporal, and Janie will be the private."

The idea seemed to fascinate them, so I continued:

"When I have a job to do, I'll give the orders to the first sergeant and he can organize a detail to do the work. The corporal and the private take their orders from the sergeant, and you have to do what he tells you. I'll hold him responsible if the work isn't done properly."

"Oh, boy," said the sergeant, "all I have to do is make them work."

"No," I said hastily, "that's not the idea at all. You're supposed to be the leader. You have to do your share of the work, to set them a good example."

"Oh," he replied, obviously much let down.

[27]

"But you'll get more pay than the others. Each of you gets paid according to rank, and since you'll do the most work, you get the most pay."

And so it became the first sergeant's duty to get everyone up by 7:30 A.M. and to see that beds were made, clothes hung up, faces washed, and hands clean in time for breakfast at 8:00 A.M. The commander-in-chief would inspect personnel and equipment before serving breakfast and after the meal he would give the first sergeant his work orders for the morning. There was a little light duty during the afternoon and a period of organized recreation—swimming, fishing, or games.

I was distressed to find that the children depended upon comic books for reading matter and on the radio thrillers for story material. So I undertook an education program in the army. An hour was set aside every afternoon when the older children were given books and a place to lie down. Within a short time, their interest had shifted from *Colonel Atom*, the *Drip Comic Crime Smasher*, to *Tom Sawyer* and *Heidi*. By a curious coincidence, the army's outdoor recreation hour always fell at the time when the bloodiest deeds were being done on the children's radio programs, so the kids missed these.

At the end of the day, the house still looked as if a cyclone had hit it, so I posted a sign which said:

"Curfew for all toys at 7:30 P.M. Any toys found out after curfew will be subject to arrest by the Military Police."

And after the MP's had put a couple of toys in the cooler for indeterminate sentences, the house began to look fairly neat before the army turned in of an evening. In fact, life in general began to run so smoothly that I actually came to believe that I had spoken a great truth when I had told my mother that it was just a question of organization.

[28]

The first little cloud on the horizon appeared one day when Janie came to tell me that she was tired of being the private.

"Ever'body gives *me* orders," she pouted.

"You've been doing such a good job that I've been meaning to promote you," I said, after a moment's thought. "From now on you can be a private first class and get a nickel more pay every week."

"But who'll be private?" she asked.

"Tinker," I said. "Tinker can be the private and then you can have somebody to give orders to."

"But Tinker's uh dog. How can uh dog be in uh army?"

"Sure she can. Ask Larry to tell you about the K-9 corps."

This seemed to satisfy her and she went back to her place in the ranks in a happier frame of mind. I congratulated myself on having used sound psychology, but it appeared that I was foolishly optimistic. For when the human heart craves justice, a mere rearrangement of the existing order of injustice does not really suffice.

But, as time went by, I began to understand what Janie was really protesting against. The first sergeant had established a sort of comic opera tyranny over his charges. He became the funny-paper personification of the tough-guy top sergeant. He never spoke to the girls, but always barked at them. He was enjoying his position of power immensely, but I could see revolt brewing in the ranks.

The girls began to get balky and to talk back to him and, as much as my sympathies lay with them, I felt that I had to back up Larry's authority. I got them back into line for a time and tried to persuade him to take a sweet and reasonable approach. But he could not resist the temptation to throw his weight around.

The girls answered this time with a little gentle sabotage—some of Larry's toys began to disappear, to be found in odd places. There would be sugar in his salt dish and hop toads in his bed. He increased his iron discipline and the more they muttered, the more he enjoyed it. Finally, I took the girls aside and gave them some private advice.

"The thing he likes best," I explained, "is to be able to boss you this way. Why don't you fix it so he won't be able to boss you so much? Try to figure out what he's going to yell at you about, before he *can* yell. That'll cure him."

Lynn wrinkled her brow, then she began to see the possibilities. I sat back to watch the plot unfold. The next morning, when Larry rushed into their room at seven-thirty to begin the horrendous din with which he usually awakened his sisters, I heard him give a loud shout. Then there was silence, while he stared open-mouthed at what he beheld. The girls were up already. Furthermore, they were dressed and had made their beds and washed themselves. Larry scurried around for a few minutes, looking vainly for something he could give them an order about. But he could find nothing.

"Okay," he said grudgingly. "As soon as I get cleaned up, we'll have inspection."

The girls almost broke their necks trying to stay ahead of him for the rest of the day. But they managed to do it. When the water pail began to get empty, they'd rush over and fill it before he could order them to do it. When the rest hour came, they jumped into their beds before he could tell them to do so. When it was time for a swim, they got into their bathing suits and were ready to go before he could blow his whistle.

It was a very frustrating day for Larry and I wondered what counter-measures he would take. I found out the following morning, when he got up fifteen minutes early—in an effort to make sure he would have the pleasure of awakening them. But the girls had anticipated this maneuver and were just as ready as they had been the morning before.

"You've got to make those girls stay in bed in the morning," he complained to me.

"Why?" I asked.

"How can I have reveille if everyone is already up?"

I could sense victory already and, as the days went by, the sergeant was reduced more and more to complaining that the girls were doing their jobs too well. I was enjoying the situation thoroughly and it seemed to me that I had, at last, organized things as they should be. But after a few days of this super-efficient, practically frictionless existence, Larry came to me and said:

"This army's no fun any more."

"No? Why not?"

"Oh, I don't know. The girls won't do it right."

"I thought they were doing fine."

"It's no fun. Can't we have something else?"

"I'll have to talk to the girls," I said.

By now, their tongues were hanging out from all the anticipatory work they had been doing and they, too, were willing to call it quits. So that night we had appropriate ceremonies for disbanding an army and I paid everyone off. The kids went to bed, happy in the knowledge that there would be no contest the next morning to see who could get up and dressed first. This thought was not quite so consoling to me and I lay awake for a long time, thinking.

"Some way," I kept telling myself, "this thing can be organized. Some way."

Chapter Four

WHEN we were preparing to leave New York, I noticed a small bottle of medicine which my mother had dropped in a suitcase.

"What's this for?" I asked suspiciously.

"The doctor said it would perk up their appetites," she said, nodding toward the children. "It *is* pretty good."

"Will they take it?"

"Oh, sure. Just put it in some water. They'll never know the difference."

When I first started cooking for the children, it seemed to me that I had better give them the sort of fare they were accustomed to eating. Accordingly, our menus sparkled with such items as macaroni and cheese, meat loaf, chops, peas and carrots, green beans, canned fruits and packaged puddings. It was all I could do, at first, to get any kind of meal on the table.

To me, each effort seemed a triumph, no matter how it tasted, so when I discovered that all I got for my pains was a baleful look from the children, my morale began to sink. I tried the appetite medicine on them, but it didn't seem to convert them into young lions, hungry for my slightly soggy rarebit. Apparently the stuff wasn't much good after all—or, perish the thought, did the trouble start with the cook?

"What's the matter with the dinner?" I asked plaintively one day.

"Nothing," said Lynn.

"Well, why don't you eat?"

"Just not hungry," she said.

"But you're never hungry. Isn't this the same kind of food you're used to? Isn't it as good as what Grandmother gives you?"

"Sure," said Larry. "But *you* ought to be able to do better."

I had never looked at my cooking in that light, but the logic of this statement seemed overwhelming. It so happened that my father arrived from the city that very night with a frying chicken that Mother had brought for us. I hadn't cooked anything as complicated as chicken up to that time, but now I calmly announced to the children that we were having it for Sunday dinner, with all the trimmings.

The fact that I knew as much about cooking chicken as I knew about piloting a dirigible didn't worry me a bit. The next day, I caught some soft crabs and told the children that the menu would be revised. We would have a chicken *and* fried crab dinner. They gave me an approving look, as if to say that they knew all along that I could do it.

I began working on the meal as soon as I got the breakfast dishes done. Half an hour before it was to be served, I went out and warned my father, to make sure that he wouldn't be up on the roof covered with tar when I unveiled my masterpiece. I rounded up the children, and the smell of chicken frying kept them hanging around the kitchen door. Everyone was there and, finally, I got everything cooked at the same time, and on the table while it was still hot.

The chicken and soft crabs were brown and crisp; the beans, seasoned nicely with bacon and garlic, were tender, and the hominy grits had come through without a single lump. I had also managed some milk gravy which had the proper color and, more important, the proper flavor. The children pitched in to eat, with the first real enthusiasm I had seen them show at meal-time, and I began to feel that my three-hour ordeal in the kitchen had been worth while. Larry ate his first serving and hardly took a deep breath before diving into a second piece of chicken and some more grits and gravy. By the time he had finished this, the others were passing their plates for seconds and Larry looked around the table with interest and asked:

"Is there another piece of chicken?"

I went to the kitchen to get some more. As I passed the shelf where I kept the medicine for weak appetites, I picked up the bottle and dropped it, ever so gently, into the wastebasket. Then, some saving instinct made me reach down and fish the bottle out again. I put it way on the back of the shelf, though.

Having discovered that boredom with the same old food was the chief trouble, I began to make a few changes in our standard menus—and, after that, I watched with a fascination border-ing on horror as the children packed away the food. Since I am the type of man (fat) who likes to eat, and since I was burdened with no previous experience in cooking, I was willing to try anything.

I picked recipes off the radio, off box tops and out of advertise-ments. I found that there are almost any number of packaged and frozen concoctions which can be fixed by anyone who can measure a cup of water and strike a match to light the stove. There are ready-made pie crusts, biscuit mixes, cakes, muffins, Spanish rice, and dozens of other items which simplify cooking for the beginner. I began to improve upon these mixtures, adding a little extra shortening to the biscuit mix or dropping an extra egg into the cake mix.

For a long time, I'd been reading those recipes given out by men-about-town who Like to Cook. But the first thing I learned now was that there is a lot of difference between knowing how to cook one fancy dish and knowing how to serve a meal. Before you can qualify as a good cook, you have to learn how to start out with a lot of ingredients and get them all on the table, properly fixed and piping hot, at exactly the same time. Anyone can learn to cook a chicken in some exotic style, but you shouldn't call yourself a cook until you can serve the chicken, along with gravy, mashed potatoes, a vegetable, biscuits, and coffee, while *everything's* warm. And you should realize as well that by the time you're ready to eat your first mouthful, you'll have to jump up from the table to refill the gravy boat.

Soon I considered myself out of the beginner's class, and my children, accustomed to the sensible routine of fare in a normal household, were dazzled as deviled crabs, orange fritters, chop suey, pineapple mousse, and apple pancakes began to appear on the table. If I found the children growing tired of boiled vegetables, I would whip up a fancy casserole, cook it in the oven, and present it with a fast sales talk. The bigger build-up I could give the meal, the bigger became their appetites. I found myself cooking things just to see if I could. Every recipe —whether it was for strawberry chiffon pie or cranberry sherbert—constituted a challenge to me. To the kids, all of this was

[35]

fine. It was like Sunday every day, and excitement would spread through the house in advance of every meal as they tried to figure out what the old man would come up with next.

My mother looked askance at some of the unorthodox methods I used in an effort to introduce the so-called male efficiency to the kitchen. I watched her jaw sag when I lined up green beans in ten-deep rows and sliced them into sections in a few strokes of the butcher knife, instead of cutting the beans one at a time as she did. Her eyebrows went up when she saw that I used the coarse part of the grater to produce finely chopped onions and green peppers and the egg slicer to cut up bananas. But her bewilderment was complete when I served a pie, on the top crust of which was stamped: "Return Empty, 5¢."

"I haven't any rolling pin," I was forced to explain, "so I had to roll out the pie crust with a milk bottle."

Some cooks also love to eat, while others seem to go through all that work simply for the pleasure that eating good things imparts to those they love. I suppose the best cooks combine something of the two motives. And if one has neither of these motives, cooking must become a burdensome, fruitless task. The cook really takes extraordinary pains to create a thing which is destroyed so quickly!

I remember the first apple pie I made for the kids. It took me better than two hours in the kitchen on a hot day. Then I put it before them, with a proper sounding of trumpets, and watched as it was consumed in a few fleeting minutes. I was sitting there wondering whether it had really been worth the bother when Janie looked up, her eyes wide with happiness, and answered the question in my mind:

"Gee, Daddy, that was good. Can we have it every meal?"

The children began to get into the spirit of the thing a little too wholeheartedly. They insisted on *helping* with the cooking. I couldn't get them to start by boiling water or peeling potatoes. They would dash in excitedly with some recipe that they wanted to try out and then would tell me to step to one side.

Lynn first tried to make a pudding out of a powdered fruit flavoring she had acquired. It turned out something short of edible and, in going back over the process with her, I found that she had erred slightly in the use of cornstarch. The recipe called for two thirds of a tablespoon, which she had misread as two thirds of a cup of cornstarch. That failure cured her for a time, but Larry had to have his innings. He came up with a recipe for a graham-cracker pie crust and I offered, in no uncertain terms, to lend a hand.

"Now you count out sixteen graham crackers, as the recipe says," I instructed, "and I'll get the rest of the stuff together."

After letting him crush the crackers, I helped him mix in the butter, sugar, and vanilla that was called for. But somehow, the crumbs just wouldn't stick together. After struggling for a long time, I began to question him.

"Are you sure you didn't put too many crackers in this?" I asked. "How many did I tell you?"

"Sixteen," he said. "That's what I used—sixteen of these."

And that solved the mystery and explains how I finally wound up with two pie crusts that day. For he had counted out sixteen *double* crackers.

But all my difficulties in the kitchen paled into insignificance, eventually, before the onslaught of the greatest menace to orderly housekeeping that the world has ever known—my father. Now it must be understood that, during a long lifetime, my father has never shown any tendency to indulge in the weaknesses to which the normal flesh is heir. I have never known him to use hard language or hard liquor or even opium. He never shows more than a flicker of interest in a passing blonde and he even breaks his cigarettes in half and smokes them on a carefully regulated schedule so as to hold down his intake of nicotine.

Truly, Dad has only one over-riding vice—and that is puttering around the cottage. He putters on a big scale. Where some men build model ships from matchsticks or make old tin cans into household accessories, he works in a bigger way with sixteen-foot lengths of two-by-four lumber or iron boiler tanks weighing two tons. For the past twenty-five years he has devoted endless hours to putting this cottage up and tearing it down; installing electricity, water, and sewage systems; and moving tons of earth from one place to another.

I had always looked with tolerance upon these activities, assuming that, as weaknesses go, this one of his was better than most. But when I started trying to cook three square meals a day in the house where he was conducting his operations, I began to take a dimmer view of the whole thing. Doors would suddenly be moved and I would find the main stream of traffic moving through the kitchen. The stove would suddenly be shifted from one place to another. Pots and pans would be requisitioned for mixing pipe compound, kitchen spoons for stirring paint, and brooms for tarring the roof. Through the house would pass an endless procession of pipe lengths, shingles, and rolls of wire.

Three or four weeks after we had moved into the cottage, I heard an unusual amount of hammering, and sawing going on in the living room. At the time, I was trying to concentrate on halving a cookbook recipe and so I didn't take the trouble to rush out and see what was being demolished. When I did wander out into the room, I found that Dad, with his little hatchet and saw, had removed about one third of the side of the house. This peaked my curiosity somewhat and, without wanting to appear too inquisitive, I asked:

"What're you doing, Dad?"

"Going to put in a fireplace," he announced proudly. "Been trying to get around to it for years."

"Hm," I said, and studied the hole in the wall thoughtfully for a while. Then I said: "Didn't know you could lay brick?"

"Oh, I could do this myself, but I don't think I will. Going to get some bricklayers down from town."

"Hm," I replied. "When?"

"Oh, next week or the week after."

"Hm," I said.

Father left that Sunday, cheerfully suggesting that if it started to rain I could cover up the hole in the house with some canvas. Having the side out of the house did, of course, improve the view—no glass or screens to distort or obscure the natural beauty of our yard. Then, the children could come in through the side of the house, without using the front or back door, and I didn't have to worry about the screens being open. In fact, so many insects came in through the hole that I opened the front screen so they'd be able to find their way out. Birds, particularly, seemed to have trouble locating the place where they had entered the house.

When Dad showed up the next Friday night and announced that the bricklayers would arrive the following morning, I felt a certain sense of relief. But then he said:

"I brought down a couple of chickens and some vegetables. You can cook up a nice meal for them at midday."

This was an idea which had eluded me, until then. I thought

[39]

the workmen would certainly bring their lunches in paper bags, but apparently Dad had promised them a chicken dinner. And I was the cook!

When the workmen arrived the following morning, my worst fears were confirmed. There were three of them, and the two older men were a couple of dour characters who looked like fugitives from one of those grim Grant Wood portraits. In addition to the home-cooked dinner and the prospect of a day in the Great Out-of-Doors, it appeared that Dad had been forced to promise them double overtime in order to get them to venture so far into the country.

After a few minutes, it was obvious that the Great Out-of-Doors was not appealing to them. Neither was anything else about the job. They complained about the way the bricks were stacked up, so Dad rushed in to drag me from my kitchen duties to help rearrange the bricks before Their Highnesses walked off the job. I went back to the stove when we had finished this, but it developed that they didn't like the kind of sand we had, so it was necessary for me to drop my spatula and haul some more up from the beach. Then they found that the cement wasn't the brand they liked, so I turned the gas down under the potatoes and hot-footed it up to the store to get a different kind.

When all these obstacles had been surmounted, they finally started to work. I watched anxiously as the first few courses of brick were set in place. The chimney was going up fast, and after a couple of hours the men needed a scaffold. Dad said that he had some lumber out of which it could be built.

Now, it must be understood that my father never throws anything away. He always saves everything, on the theory that some day he will need it. Actually I think that he bought this

[40]

cottage originally in order to have a place where he could take old newspapers, broken window sashes, leaky pans, and scraps of pipe that Mother made him clean out of the basement of the house in town. So, when the bricklayers needed lumber for scaffolding, it was only natural that he would have something that he had been saving for just such a purpose. He went out into the brush and dragged in some planks which he proudly identified as the remains of a sailboat I had owned in my boyhood.

"Always knew I'd find something to do with this," he said. The bricklayers looked at him with disbelief. The lumber was perfectly sound, although weatherbeaten. But the boss bricklayer gave forth with an outburst of temperament which would have made Toscanini appear, by comparison, as calm as a Russian chess champion thinking out his second move. He took Dad to task for living, breathing, and exploiting the working class. He cursed the sand, the bricks, and the mortar and was just getting under way on the other aspects of this job when, with a look at the half-filled hole in the house, where the chimney was supposed to go, I dashed into the kitchen. Then turning all burners on the stove to high, I started to work on my dinner under forced draft. My eye fell on the long-neglected bottle of medicine for failing appetites and a fiendish inspiration hit me. I dumped most of it into a pitcher of well water, grabbed some glasses, and dashed outside. I poured three glasses of water and handed them to the workmen.

"Here," I said. "You must be hot out here."

"I'm plenty hot, all right," said the boss bricklayer, "and it ain't just the weather. What I ever drove sixty-five miles down here for, to have somebody tell me I ought to work on a scaffold made out of wood like that for, I don't know. The sand's no good. Just don't make the mortar run right. And I can't do nothing with brick like that, why man . . ."

He stopped raving long enough to drink his glass of water and I beat it back to the kitchen. I could hear the whole crew fussing and fuming, and then they started to pack their tools for the return trip to town. I was cooking potatoes and chicken and gravy with more speed, skill, and determination than I had applied to anything in years. Just as the three of them clapped on their hats and started for the car, I dashed out.

"Dinner's ready," I called out. "Fried chicken."

They exchanged dark looks and I knew that this was the critical moment—either the medicine, and a few hours out-doors, had given them a terrific appetite, or else we weren't going to have a chimney. Just then, a puff of wind carried the smell of the frying chicken past their noses. That did it.

Still grumbling, they started toward the house. They washed and went to the table, and I watched anxiously as they started nibbling suspiciously at the platter of chicken. They plainly expected that it would be, like everything else they had en-countered around our place that day, something less than satis-factory. They tasted the mashed potatoes as if they feared they might have ground glass in them and sniffed at the sliced tomatoes and cucumbers before touching them.

Then I heaved a sigh of relief as I saw them pitch in and eat exactly as three bricklayers should after a hard morning of debate. When they had cleaned up everything on the table and still sat there, looking expectant, I trotted out some home-made ice cream. They ate this and, for the first time, I could detect some relaxed lines in those faces which had seemed made of concrete.

While I was plying them with food, Dad was outside, hammering away. After they had finished smoking their fifty-cent cigars, the bricklayers strolled out casually and looked at the scaffolding that Dad had put up with the old lumber. It looked as solid as a Treasury statement and, without further equivocation, they unpacked their tools and climbed up to finish the job. They whistled at their work that afternoon and, when Dad paid them off, the boss said he was sorry he had got so mad. It had really been a fine day and he didn't remember when he'd been so hungry and had such a good meal.

Dad and I stood for a while, looking at the chimney. Then we walked into the house.

"There wasn't anything wrong with that scaffold," he said. "It was exactly the kind of lumber we needed. Just like I always say, if you save things long enough, you'll find a use for them."

"I guess you're right," I said, catching myself in the act of dropping the appetite medicine back into the wastebasket.

I restored it to the shelf in the kitchen. You never can tell when Dad's going to decide that we need another chimney.

Chapter Five

BY now, the winds of autumn had begun to whistle around my cottage door. It was early September, and I had been housekeeping for nearly two months. During that time I had cooked 168 meals; had made 13 pies (5 with meringue); had baked 493 biscuits, with no recorded fatalities; had made 187 beds, washed 1,834,851 dishes (estimated), walked the equivalent of six times around the world without leaving my own house, and had swept enough dirt off the floor to fill the crater of Mt. Vesuvius. My trouble was that, having accomplished this by working no more than eighteen hours a day, I had developed delusons of grandeur. There seemed to be nothing I couldn't do.

Because autumn, the season which usually precedes winter, had arrived, I informed the children that we would have to go back to the nice, warm city. Their howls of anguish were genuine, prolonged, and repeated.

"No," said Janie firmly. "I wanta stay here, wif alla sand."

When Janie spoke, it was with some authority—because she had become the head of a large family. She now had twelve dolls, all of them named Tweenie. When she said she liked the sand, she meant that all twelve Tweenies also liked the sand.

"But it's going to get cold here," I said. "And you kids have to go back to school."

"Aw, you know more than any old teacher," said Larry. "Why don't you teach us at home?"

"Yes, Daddy, yes," shouted Lynn, jumping up and down.

"I'll teach my dolls," said Janie. "You won't have to do 'at."

It was in this way that my delusions of grandeur led me astray. Because the idea of teaching the children at home did not stagger me in the least. Instead, it seemed a rather trivial undertaking for a man who had learned to make strawberry meringues and to darn socks and plait French braids. I didn't agree immediately, but when the middle of September arrived and I had found no place in the city to live, I called the children together.

"I've written to some people in Florida," I told them. "And maybe we can go down there for the winter. I don't think there's much use in starting school around here, so we'll just study at home for a couple of weeks."

The following day, I found a blackboard in the attic and rang the bell for school promptly at nine o'clock. It was not until I found myself with my back to a blank blackboard and my face turned toward the student body that I began to wonder what I was going to do next.

"Where did you leave off last year?" I asked the children. They gave me blank looks.

"I mean, what were you studying? In arithmetic, for instance."

"I was through my five tables, I think," said Lynn.

"We were going to have decimals," said Larry.

Now, ever since my own school days, I have carefully maintained nothing more than a nodding acquaintance with decimals.

"Suppose we just review a little," I suggested. "We'll go back over your multiplication tables. Lynn, you start."

She recited them slowly and I nodded approval when she had finished.

"Well, you seem to know them all right," I said.

"She made a mistake," said Larry. "Four times nine isn't thirty-eight."

"All right," I said defensively. "What is four times nine?"

"Thirty-four," he said proudly.

"It is not," Lynn said in triumph.

"It is so."

"It is not."

"Ask Daddy, then."

I had been holding out for thirty-five, but we finally settled for thirty-six and then went on to Larry's recitation of the multiplication tables. I suspected he was giving me some wrong answers, but by the time I could figure out what seven times nine really was, he would have gone on to eight times six and I'd have to figure again to see whether his answer to that was right.

"That's pretty good," I said, not being able to find any more pertinent comment to make.

"Gee, you're a good teacher, Daddy," Larry said. "Now can we do some fractions?"

Not knowing the top side of a fraction from the bottom, I decided that I'd better go into a clinch and stall for time.

"I've got to fix dessert," I said. "You help Lynn with her tables."

[46]

This occupied them for half an hour and after that I called a recess. This took care of another fifteen minutes, but it still was only ten-thirty and I knew that school had to last longer than that.

"We'll study English next," I said learnedly. "What do they teach you? Prepositions and things like that?"

"I don't know," said Lynn. "What's a preposition?"

"Why, it's a—well, a preposition is a little word that—oh, well, if you don't know what a preposition is, you couldn't be that far along anyway."

"What's a conjunction?" Larry demanded.

"It's a word that—well, it connects. . . . I just don't know how to explain these things simply enough for you children to understand. Maybe if I got the dictionary . . ."

"The dog tore up the dictionary last week," said Larry. "Remember when you got so mad you spanked her with the pancake turner?"

"That was mean of you," said Lynn, pouting.

I was pawing the air mentally. Having made a living for several years writing the English language, or some sub-species thereof, I now found myself unable to instruct my children in its use. Then Lynn let forth a yell.

"He hit me with an inkball," she said.

I turned to glower at Larry.

"I did not," he said righteously. "It was a spitball."

"*My* children are good in school," said Janie, who was conducting a class in crayon drawing in the corner for the twelve Tweenies.

"Well, mine had better start being good," I said. "Now let's get on the ball. How about some history?"

[47]

"You never did tell us what a conjunction was," said Larry.

"That comes later," I said sternly. "You just worry about what we're having now. Do you children study history?"

"No, but we have geography."

"I'd have to get a book, to teach you geography," I said. "In fact, I guess we're going to have to get some books for everything."

I sent a hurried note to my father that day, asking him to bring down an assortment of textbooks when he came for the week end. Meanwhile, by ransacking the cottage, I did manage to find an old book on penmanship and a French grammar, reminders of my bright resolve in some bygone years to study during summer vacations. So, for the rest of the week, we specialized in the arithmetic tables, penmanship, and elementary French.

Every day, I went to the post office in the hope that I would get an answer from one of the house-wanted letters I had sent to Florida. It had suddenly occurred to me that, by keeping the children home from school, I was breaking the law. As the days went by, this fear enlarged itself until I began to feel like a criminal hiding out in the woods. I kept the children at home during school hours, because I was afraid they would attract too much attention if allowed to run loose. Every time I heard a car on the road, I looked up quickly to see whether it was the truant officer coming after us.

It was extraordinary, therefore, that when a car did pull into our yard one morning, I didn't even hear it. Perhaps it was because I was in the midst of a French lesson and my French is rather explosive, especially to the trained ear.

"Où est la plume?" I was asking, when I looked up and saw a pleasant-looking woman standing on the front steps.

[48]

"Oh, come in," I said.

The lady told me her name and explained that she lived down the road from us. I recalled that I knew her husband, who was the telegraph operator in the county seat. Our conversation was getting off to a fine start until she said:

"I'm a member of the school board in this district."

My heart bounced off the top of my stomach. Well, I thought, I guess they've got me. Suddenly, I became conscous of my costume—it was a hot day and I was doing my teaching in the apparel normal for me on such a day—a pair of shorts. Now I hitched them up nervously.

"We've just got a small school here," she said. "Only two teachers. And they say that they'll have to cut us down to one teacher if we don't get our quota of pupils."

She talked on and I was very sympathetic.

"How many children do you need to make your quota?" I asked, at length.

"Just two more," she said, smiling sweetly. "And I thought that if you folks were going to be staying down here . . ."

"I'm expecting to leave for Florida almost any day," I said hastily. "And I just don't think it would be worth while to start the children for such a short time."

She was plainly disappointed and, it seemed to my guilty mind, a bit skeptical. Quickly I tried to change the subject and started to ask about her husband.

"He's working awfully hard," she said.

"Lots of business at Western Union?" I asked.

"Oh no. He only works there part time now. But he's the truant officer for the county and that keeps him hopping."

I gulped.

"There must be a lot of truancy, then?" I said politely.

"Heavens—the excuses people invent to keep their children out of school!"

"Well, do give him my best regards."

"I'll do that," she said, rising to leave. "Maybe he'll be down to see you one of these days."

She departed then, leaving me to ponder this cryptic remark. The more I pondered, the more I worried. Finally, I called off school for the day and sat down to write some more letters to friends in Florida—air mail, special delivery.

The winds of October, meanwhile, were beginning to sneak through the cracks in our cottage and I was almost a nervous wreck. I spent so much time looking out for the truant officer that I can't imagine how that car sneaked up into the yard again without my seeing it.

This time, I was doing arithmetic tricks, which I had learned from one of the books that Dad had brought us. The children infinitely preferred tricks to such routine matters as multiplication and division, and they were roaring with delight when I glanced up to see two women standing on the steps. One was my friend from the school board and the other was introduced as the principal of the local grammar school.

"I see you're still teaching them," said my friend.

"Yes," I gulped. "Just day to day. Don't know when we'll have to pull out suddenly."

"They seem to get quite a kick out of their arithmetic," said the teacher.

"Just a little sugar coating," I said. "We have our serious moments, too."

"But this is better than school," said Larry, aggressively.

"What's the matter with school?" asked the principal.

"Aw, we're used to city schools," Larry replied.

[50]

"I thought that if you met Miss Louise," said the lady from the school board, "you might be able to make the children feel differently about our little school."

"Oh, it's not that . . ." I started to explain.

"I don't want to go to a country school," Larry insisted.

"We do our best," said the principal. "It's not what you children are used to, of course."

"Daddy teaches us French," Larry went on, ignoring the scowls I was throwing in his direction. "Daddy knows everything."

"Oh," said the principal brightly, "tu parles francais?"

When I hear anyone pronounce three words of French as impeccably as she had, I always back away and insist I don't understand a word of the language. But not Larry. He stuck out his jaw stubbornly and said:

"Oui."

This, of course, led her to start talking to him in French, faster than a Parisian gendarme giving road directions. Larry's jaw sagged and his face took on a blank look.

"What did she say?" he asked finally.

"She was talking to you in French," I said. "You told her you could speak French."

"I can," he insisted. "But what did she say? I just didn't understand her."

"The sum and substance of it," I conjectured, "was that for a little boy, you talk too much."

The two ladies resumed their gentle efforts to interest me in sending the children to school. I tried to convince them that I didn't have anything against schools in general, nor theirs in particular—it was just that I didn't expect to spend much more time in Maryland. But I probably sounded more defensive than sincere because I kept reminding myself that I was talking to the wife of the county truant officer. They departed, finally, and I went back to teaching.

This time, I resolved to double my lookout for the truant officer, for I was convinced that he would descend upon me at any moment. Since I was watching the road so closely now, I was able to see him the minute he came around. I was teaching at the time, but now I suddenly remembered something important I must do in the attic.

"If anyone calls," I flung back at the children, "say you don't know exactly when I'll be back."

A few minutes later, I heard the children talking to the man and then I heard the door close.

"I reckon he'll be back pretty soon," he said. "I didn't pass him on the road."

Then he sat down to wait. I peeked down from the attic and I could see that he was holding a piece of paper which, from where I was looking, appeared to be a summons.

"So you like to stay home from school?" he asked the children.

They said that they certainly did, and went on to picture the beauties of life as they were leading it.

"Be pretty hard for you to get used to school again, I reckon," he said, with the tone of a man who had some advance knowledge on the subject.

The fellow plainly had his sitting britches on and there didn't seem to be much point in my staying in the attic any longer. So I climbed down, made a sheepish apology for my absence, and prepared for the worst.

"I've got something for you," our visitor announced cheerfully.

"Have you?" I asked tremulously.

"You'll be glad to get this, I reckon," he said. "It came in just as I was leaving the telegraph office, so I thought I'd bring it down to you."

He handed me a telegram, which I read quickly:

"Have furnished cottage at fifty-five dollars monthly. Near stores and school. Wire if you want it."

It was signed by one of the friends to whom I had written in Florida.

For a minute I was too stunned to speak, but then I recovered and asked my visitor:

"When you get finished rounding up these scoundrels who won't go to school today, are you going back to the telegraph office?"

"I reckon so," he said. "Want to send an answer to this?"

"I sure do. Just send a message back to this same fellow and sign my name."

"Don't you want to write out the message?"

"It's very simple," I said, and sighed. "Just one word—'YES.' "

Chapter Six

ON a frosty November afternoon, we boarded one of those sit-up streamliners, bound for Florida—boarded it like a pirate crew taking over an unarmed merchantman. A hush fell over our coach as I swept in with my flying circus and, for all of thirty seconds, the children stared around the car in wondering silence. Then, with a series of loud explosions, they got back to normal. Within fifteen minutes they had put both of the car's drinking fountains out of commission, had tripped the candy butcher, and had started a small flood in the ladies' room. It was beginning to look as if the railroads were in for their most spectacular disaster since the wreck of the Old 99.

But I was not entirely unprepared, for I had brought along a collection of games, puzzles, and comics. So I sat on the children long enough to get them interested in a program of relatively quiet entertainment. A sailor on one of the seats behind us joined in and we managed to keep the children occupied until we reached Richmond. By this time, they had completely exhausted me, the sailor, and my fund of parlor games.

"I'm going to the club car," the sailor announced. "This is too rough for me."

"Can I go with him, Daddy?" asked Larry.

"Sure," said the sailor. "I'll buy you a bottle of milk."

Their departure made room for the rest of us. The car was full and with four of us squeezed into two double seats, there had been just room enough to breathe. Now I made Janie stretch out on one of the seats and tucked her dolls in around her. She seemed restless, and after a little while she called to me.

"Daddy," she whispered. "Daddy, I feel funny."

Helplessly I began to look around the car. The human race has accorded fathers all the necessary privileges—except the right to take small daughters into the ladies' room. I was trying to decide whether Lynn would be able to handle this situation when the whole matter became more or less academic. Because Janie got sick right there, where she was. It took the porter, two kind old ladies, and the train nurse to get everything straightened up, but finally we made the child comfortable.

"I hope my dolls don't get sick, too," she said sadly. "'At would be uh awful mess for you, Daddy."

An hour later she was sound asleep and Lynn was getting drowsy. I suddenly began to wonder what had ever happened to Larry and the sailor. So I left Lynn to watch over her sister and started out for the club car, where I found Larry and his friend. The sailor had finished thirteen bottles of beer and Larry was on his fourth bottle of milk when I appeared.

"Oh, boy, what a mess," I told the sailor. "The little girl got sick."

"You're going to be kinda crowded, ain't you?" he asked. "Only two seats for the four of you?"

"Oh, we'll make out all right, I guess," I said wearily. "Some way."

[56]

"Can I stay here all night?" Larry asked.

I told him that he could stay for a little while longer and I went back to the girls. Then I persuaded Lynn to lie down on our other seat and she was asleep in a few minutes. That left nowhere for me to sit, so I went to the smoking compartment to wait for Larry. He came back after a time and sat with me. I sent him out to look at the girls a little later and he reappeared to announce:

"Gee, Daddy, everybody must have gotten off the train. There's nobody left in our end of the car."

"Maybe you can find some place to sleep, then," I suggested.

I walked back with him and found that our end of the car, which had been packed solid an hour before, was now deserted. The sailor was stretched out on an entire seat, dead to the world, with his feet dangling in the aisle. Larry and I picked out seats and went to sleep.

It was still rather dark outside when I woke up, learned our station was next, and began to pick up our baggage. The car was dimly lighted and I found everything, except one of the dolls named Tweenie.

"I forgot," said Janie. "She got sick last night and I lef' her in uh bafroom."

The sailor was still snoring peacefully and Larry was all for waking him up so that we could say good-bye, but I persuaded him it was better to let sleeping gobs lie. We went to the coach vestibule to wait for the train to pull into our station, but there was a slight delay—a palm tree had grown up between the tracks, or something.

While we were standing there, the sailor appeared suddenly, looking as fresh as a pound of Grandma's country butter. He spotted us and grew exuberant.

[57]

"I was looking for you," he said. "You getting off here?"

"If we ever get to 'here,'" I said.

"Rough voyage, huh," he said. "Did you get some sleep all right?"

"Finally."

"How'd you like the way I cleaned that car out for you?"

"Did you do that?"

"Sure," he grinned. "I started the rumor that the little girl had chicken pox and they all beat it to the lounge car."

He laughed and leaned down to pat Janie on the back. Suddenly, he straightened up, his grin at half mast.

"Hey," he said. "Look at the kid—she *has* got something."

I leaned over quickly and inspected her. In the sunlight which was coming through the train door, I could see something that had eluded me in the half-lighted coach.

"She's got something, all right," I said. "And it *does* look like chicken pox."

"My aching back," whooped the sailor. "And I ain't never had it."

At this moment, the train ground to a stop and the porter opened the door. I grabbed the children and tumbled down the steps.

"So long," I yelled to the sailor, but there was no answer.

A few seconds later, I found myself standing on the platform of a small railroad station, entirely surrounded and up to my chin in baggage and children, at least one of whom had a communicable disease. I looked around hopefully for my friend John, who had promised to meet us. He was not there and my heart sank. Then I noticed a couple of young men hurrying toward us.

"You must be the folks we're looking for," one of them said.

Then he went on to explain that John had been called away and had asked them to meet us. They were to take us out to John's house, where we were to stay until we could get into our own place.

"Ever had chicken pox?" I asked, when they had finished their explanations.

After I told them our troubles, they immediately took charge. They drove us to John's house, got a doctor, obtained medicine, brought us food, and called for Tinker, the puppy, at the express office.

"Gee, they're nice to us," said Lynn, after watching these two total strangers devote an entire day to our welfare.

"That's southern hospitality," I explained.

"What's that mean?" she asked.

"Down here, people are very kind to strangers and do courteous things for them. You children must remember that and you must be extra polite while you're here."

After I had unpacked the groceries which John's friends had brought in, I discovered that I was faced with a new problem. John is a bachelor and he had written that he was doing his own cooking, when he felt like eating at home. I could see immediately that this was not very often. The only equipment I could find in the kitchen, when I began to fix dinner, was a coffee pot, a frying pan, some cups, three spoons, two forks, one knife, and an inexhaustible supply of highball glasses.

Apparently, if you got a spoon you didn't get a fork, and that gave everyone at least one piece of silver. But the knife was a problem, and in the middle of dinner that evening I found myself impressing upon Larry a very delicate, even dubious, point of etiquette.

"Hey, who's got the knife?" he demanded.

"That's not good manners," I said. "You should say 'Please pass the knife.'"

"What's that?" he asked, "some more of this southern hospitality?"

But, as the days went by, we saw more and more of the kindness which is sometimes showered on strangers in the South. John's friends poured in with presents for the children and offers of help. We were supplied with home-made soup and cakes, flowers and candy, extra silver and extra linen without end. Someone who had been hunting dropped by to ask us if we wanted a couple of squirrels he had shot.

"I don't like squirrel," said Larry, firmly.

"I don't think you should have shot the cute little things," Lynn said sadly.

"'At was mean," Janie chimed in.

But I accepted them with many thanks and, after our visitor had left, I scolded the children.

"You weren't at all courteous," I said. "That was some more southern hospitality and, even if you didn't want us to have the squirrels, you should have been nice enough to thank the man and act as if you were glad. If you don't act nice about these things, whether you want them or not, people will get their feelings hurt."

While I was spending most of my time around the house, watching over the chicken pox case, Larry and Lynn were out exploring the neighborhood. They had both had chicken pox when they were younger, so they were in no danger. In their journeys, they found an alligator farm which they visited once a day and an orange juice stand, which they visited twice a day. It was one of those places which advertised "All the Orange Juice U-Can-Drink—10 cents." I would give each of them a dime when they set out after breakfast and another dime when they left after lunch and would forget about their citrus vitamins beyond that. One day, they didn't ask for their dimes after lunch and I wanted to know why.

"The man said we could only come once a day from now on," Lynn told me.

"Why?" I asked. "Haven't you children been polite?"

"Well," Lynn said thoughtfully, "he told us that since we came here, he'd been losing money."

"Aw, he's just an old sourpuss," Larry blustered. "Why, Lynn hardly ever drank more than six glasses at a time."

"And ten was the most you ever drank," said Lynn.

Tinker, the beagle, had acclimated herself just as quickly as the children. She followed them sometimes on their journeys, but when they visited the alligators she would trot around the neighborhood with great aplomb, her white-tipped tail held high in the air. One afternoon, she went off with the children but, when they returned, she wasn't following them. They said that she had started home an hour before, and so we set out to look for the dog. I went toward the woods behind John's house and Larry walked over toward the highway that ran some two hundred yards away. He had been gone only a short time when I heard him cry:

"Daddy! Daddy!"

There was more anguish in that cry than I ever remember hearing in a human voice. It stabbed right into my heart and I knew the whole story right away. I started running toward the boy as fast as I could. His call grew into a sob. When I reached him, he was standing beside the little dog's body at the side of the road. Tinker had been run over by someone who had been in too much of a hurry to care much about little boys' dogs. Larry was standing over her, crying, and I took him in my arms. I felt as if my chest would burst with anguish.

After leading him back to the house I had to tell the girls what had happened. Then, fighting back tears of my own, I went out to bury Tinker. When I got back to the house, the children were wailing at the top of their lungs. Hopelessly, I tried to console them, but finally I broke down and joined in myself.

It was two or three hours before we could pull ourselves together. Not wanting to face the prospect of sitting around the house and mourning for hours, I packed the children into John's car and took them into town. Janie had passed out of the contagious stage by now and so we went to the movies. It was a double feature, which mercifully seemed to last forever. When it was over, everyone had stopped crying and I knew that my problem would be to keep anyone from starting again. I groped around for some silver lining, some bright promise that would keep the children's spirits up.

"I tell you what," I said, as we drove home, "why don't we start a beagle kennel up in Maryland. We'll name it after Tinker —call it the Tinker Kennels. Then we can have lots and lots of little beagles running around."

I don't know what made me broach the idea—because I had been vowing, until that moment, that we would never have another pet of any kind. I thought that I couldn't face the death of another of them. But the children brightened up so much when I began to spin my tale that I just had to keep on talking.

"Could we call them all Tinker?" Larry asked.

"How would they know when to come?" Lynn demanded.

"You'd call one Tinker and the bunch of them'd come running."

"My dolls know," said Janie, solemnly. " 'Ey all have uh same name."

"No," I said, "why not just give them names that begin with 'T'—like Tippy, and Topper, and maybe Tonker."

The children were enchanted now, so we went on building up this paradise for beagle hounds, where there would be no automobiles, but plenty of rabbits to chase. Somehow, it took a lot of the sting out of the whole tragedy and almost made me weaken in my resolve to have no more pets.

After I had put the children to bed that evening, three of John's friends called on me. I told the ladies the story of our day and they seemed to be deeply distressed. The following morning, one of them came back.

"I woke up thinking about those poor children," she told me. "I just had to come over and ask you all to come down for dinner today."

I accepted and spent the morning getting the children presentable.

"Now, for heaven's sake, remember your manners," I warned them. "You're going to get some more southern hospitality and I want you to be very polite. If they have something for dinner that you don't like, eat it anyway and act as if you enjoyed it. We don't want to hurt their feelings."

I was glad that I had coached the children, because the dinner included the only vegetable for which all of them have an aversion—squash. I saw Lynn toying with hers, trying to push it over to one side of her plate. I looked at her sternly and, during a lull in the conversation, said slowly:

"Isn't this *southern hospitality* wonderful!"

Whether it was my glare or the code words, I don't know, but she got the idea and started to eat her squash immediately.

[63]

"Nice squash," said Larry, horning into the routine.

"I don't like squash," said Janie, "But 'is time, I do."

I beamed happily and after dinner our hostess said she wanted to take the children for a ride.

"I'll take them over to my sister's," she said. "They've got a lot of children over there."

So without further ado she packed them into her car and started off. Half an hour later they came back, and the children were shouting excitedly.

I looked at them, my hair stood on end, and then I calmed them down long enough to hear their story.

"We went out to her sister's house," Lynn said. "And they had lots and lots of cats. There were a lot of children, too. So her sister asked us if we'd like to have a cat and I said sure, it would sort of take Tinker's place. So the lady yelled to her children: 'All right, everybody, grab your own cat.' So all the children picked up their kittens and there were just these two little ones left over. So we decided to take both of them. Aren't they cute?"

" 'Is one is mine," said Janie, holding up a frightened baby cat.

The kittens seemed to be about six weeks old and were identical twins. They had black faces, white chests, and white feet and looked like nothing so much as a couple of minstrel-show comedians dressed in tuxedoes. All this was very nice, but I reminded myself that I was a man who was through with pets and especially *two* pets and especially two *cats*. However, before I could rear back and speak a loud 'no' our hostess bustled in.

"I bet you're just furious with me," she said, laughing. "I simply couldn't help it, when I saw how much your children wanted the kittens. I'll take them back if you don't want the kids to have them."

Just then, Lynn looked at me archly and spoke the fatal words:

"It's southern hospitality, Daddy."

"Can we keep 'em, Daddy?" asked Janie.

"Why," I said, choking a little, "of course you can keep them. Now don't forget to say 'thank you ever so much.' We certainly are glad to get them."

Everyone smiled happily at that, except the kittens and me. We sat there quietly, exchanging looks of mutual suspicion.

Chapter Seven

MY friend John is a very friendly fellow, indeed. He collects people like a shaggy dog gathers burrs in the fall. He is always hurrying somewhere and, as he speeds along, he picks up people. He will start the day with only a couple of people, who are left over from the night before. Then, as the afternoon and evening progress, he enlarges the group. By lunch time, he is moving with a squad; by dinner time, with a platoon, and by midnight, he has a company—or on Saturdays, a battalion. He likes people in all shapes, sizes, and forms. John will furnish conversation and food. The only requirement he makes of people is that they be able to feed themselves. Anything else, he is willing to do for his friends. Some people stay friends with John for a long time, while others do not follow him around for very long.

The reason for this is that my friend John is a very well-meaning fellow. He is always trying to do favors for people. But John can't really do as many favors as he tries to do. Some small-minded people get angry when John fails them and say that if that's the best he can do, they'll never let him do any more favors for them. I had been friends with John for a long time, because I had almost never let him do any favors for me, or not any important ones, anyway.

When I wrote and asked John to get us a house in Florida, it was the first important favor I had ever asked of him, I believe. I was so desperate then, what with the truant officer breathing down my neck, that I rather overlooked my past resolves. Now, we were living in John's house, which was another favor, and we were waiting for him to get back to town so that he could take us out to the house he had rented for us.

Even without John, life wasn't dull in his house. A lot of people didn't know that he was out of town, so we had a fairly steady stream of visitors. I would step out of the shower and find one of John's friends in the bathroom shaving, with *my* razor, naturally. The doorbell would ring at 1, 3, and 7 A.M. I finally decided to leave the door open at night, and then it was just a question of how many people we'd find sleeping on the living-room floor in the morning. We never served breakfast to anyone who didn't bring a knife, though, because we four Toombs were having a tough enough time getting along with John's one knife as it was.

John came roaring into town, at last, arriving at three o'clock in the morning and escorted by a Congressman, two sailors, a Marine Colonel, three members of the brass section of an all-girl orchestra, and two state policemen. The rest of the gang, he explained happily, would be along later. John immediately started to straighten out my life. He decided that I was going to bed too early and living too much to myself and that all of this would have to change.

"Could you show me where our house is, tomorrow?" I asked, a little nervously. "I mean, today . . ."

"No hurry," he said happily. "You all just stay here for a while

[67]

and meet some of the people. We can have a wonderful re-union."

"John," I said quietly and desperately. "I'm the father of three. Mother, too. Things aren't like they used to be when we were young and gay. You just tell me where the place is and I'll move out there this morning."

I managed to get John out of bed by three o'clock that afternoon, without waking the two sailors. They were the only characters left from the evening before who had been able to resist the children's early-morning efforts on behalf of moderation. We set out to see the new house, but on the way we had to stop and visit some of John's friends who were, he thought, expecting him for lunch.

We found that they were expecting him for *dinner*, instead, and when they saw him arriving two hours early, and with four extra mouths to feed, they suffered near apoplexy. We managed to leave fairly quickly and were halfway to our destination when John decided that he must have some breakfast.

We went into a roadhouse night club where he seemed to be well known because we were given the run of the place. Since this was a night club, they hadn't any food prepared yet so John decided to breakfast on beer and ice cream. The children took turns serving each other cokes across the bar. When John asked Janie to draw him a short beer, I decided that the children's life with this happy, carefree bachelor was going to be educational—although not necessarily in the approved direction—and I hustled the whole mob out of the place forthwith.

"I hope you'll like this house," said John as we drove on. "It's in a little summer-resort town."

This description interested me. From the advertisements I knew that Florida was a tropical paradise in the winter. And I had assumed that the state was completely deserted in the summer, except for real-estate salesmen in hibernation, watchmen, beachcombers, and a few frumpy waitresses who served watered liquor to the beachcombers. But John informed me that things weren't this way at all—that there was winter, when it was sometimes cold, and summer, when it was always hot. Florida, it appeared, was full of people at all seasons of the year.

We had reached the edge of a pretty little lake and turned down a street that led between rows of cottages. He stopped at the edge of the lake, in front of a drab, brown frame house.

"I'll get the landlord for you," John said, walking toward the next house.

A few minutes later, we entered our new home.

"We usually rent this place by the week," said the landlord. "Just in the summer."

A quick glance at the living room made this remark more understandable. For the place was furnished with nothing more than the bare essentials and they were really bare. There were a couple of chairs and a settee, which established the decorative motif—a sort of William Jennings Bryan wicker. The living-room rug was made of grass—faded, stained, and featuring a large hole in the center. There were no curtains, and this emphasized the fascinating window-blind arrangement. The wooden sticks had been torn out of the bottom of all of the blinds and, as a result, no two were the same length.

The children dived into a closet, looking through the souvenirs left behind by the previous tenants. I stared at the ceiling, where a single electric bulb hung. It was the only possible source of artificial light in the place. I asked the landlord, a little timidly:

"Is there some sort of floor lamp?"

"All that goes with the place is just what you see," he answered simply and finally.

"No floor lamps?"

"Just what you see."

John was beginning to fidget.

"Gotta friend across the street," he said. "Maybe I can borrow a lamp from him. I'll run over there."

The place looked as bare as the Gobi Desert, but I had learned by now that one did not wave a red flag in front of a landlord. So I tried to be very tactful.

"Is there some sort of table?" I asked, looking around the living room. "Sort of a place I could use to work?"

"Just what you see," he said, nodding toward the corner. There was a card table folded up there. I opened the legs—all three of them—and leaned it against the wall.

"Nice fireplace," I said cheerfully. Then, remembering that John had mentioned that Florida really had cold weather, I asked: "Guess it keeps the place nice and warm."

"There was some people here last winter for a while," he said. "They kept warm, yes, suh."

"Never gets too cold here anyway, I guess."

He shrugged and did not commit himself.

"No stove or anything beside the fireplace?" I asked, getting a little apprehensive now.

"Just what you see."

I looked at the bedroom and then the kitchen-dining alcove. The supply of dishes, silver, and cooking utensils was small.

[70]

The landlord said I was expected to bring my own. Idly, I tried the water taps in the sink. The cold water ran, but nothing came out of the hot-water taps. I went into the bathroom and tried the hot-water taps there, with the same result.

"Guess you've got the hot water shut off," I said amiably.

"No, suh," the landlord said. Then he uttered an understatement which has probably never been surpassed. "Hot water is the *one* thing we don't have in this house."

I was surveying the scene with foreboding when Larry came whizzing by, waving a Confederate flag and shouting "Dixie," off-key, at the top of his lungs.

"Look what I found in the closet," he shouted.

Lynn and Janie screeched out the front door in their bathing suits and I noticed the landlord's brow knitting up in a dubious frown.

"Sand! Sand!" Janie was shouting.

"Have you got a fountain pen?" I said quickly. "I'll write out a check for the first month's rent."

While I was doing this, John came in the front door, dragging a floor lamp behind him.

"Look what I found in Freddie's garage," he said triumphantly, standing it up. "He said you could use it."

I looked at the lamp. It might have seen better days, but certainly never worse ones. It leaned crazily to port, and this eccentricity caused me to study the rest of the room. The card table was leaning in the opposite direction, namely starboard. The chairs sagged down and the rug curled up. The blinds hung at all levels, looking as tattered as a Monday wash on the wrong side of the tracks. For the first time, I noticed that there was a bookcase in the room. It had been made out of old orange crates and it leaned to port, also. As my eyes went from one thing to another, I swayed unconsciously, trying to make the furniture seem vertical.

"What's the matter?" John asked, as he saw me leaning in one direction, then another.

"Nothing," I said. "Nothing."

Larry and Lynn started to school the next day and I was relieved to find that, despite their erratic educational life that fall, they were ahead of the other children in all of their subjects. A young wife in the community was running a nursery school for the young children and I enrolled Janie. Then, for the first time in many a month, I discovered what peace and quiet was like. It was even possible for me to do some writing on a regular schedule.

I was born in the South and spent the early years of my childhood there. My fondest memories of those days embrace the good things we had to eat. Back in the South now, and operator of a kitchen of my own, I ran amok in the field of southern cooking. Greens boiled with white bacon, spoonbread, black-eyed peas, hog jowl, cane syrup, and syllabub became featured attractions on our menu. I established to my own satisfaction that the southern way is the only proper way to cook fish— drag the fish through corn meal and then fry it in deep fat— and that no fish should be served without hush puppies. These are made of a corn-meal batter, with a little finely chopped onion in it, and dropped from a tablespoon into the fat in which the fish has fried. They puff up and brown like doughnuts. Originally, these were by-products of outdoor hunting and fish fries. When the hounds would start to howl, the cook would fry up some corn-meal batter and the bread would

[72]

be thrown to the dogs with the admonition: "Hush, puppy."

The girls were slightly reticent about some of the items that appeared on our bill of fare, but Larry accepted everything southern with an enthusiasm that was a little too wholehearted for comfort. For, on the day he found the Confederate flag, Larry had discovered a new loyalty—the Lost Cause. Announcing that our family was seceding from the Union, he made some new flags out of one of my sheets and crayoned in the Stars and Bars. For a while, he could go nowhere without the rebel flag hung on the end of a broomstick and most of the time he was shouting Dixie as loud as he could. Within a couple of weeks, he had reorganized the Confederate Army, by drafting all the boys in town, and had proclaimed himself the new President of the Confederate States of America. To such a character, of course, mustard greens, pot liquor, and cracklin' bread were the staff of life.

My kitchen and the equipment with which I had to work would have given Betty Crocker the screaming fits inside of three minutes. But after my stretch in John's one-knife house, this place seemed luxuriously appointed. Most of the pans were either iron skillets or tin corn-bread pans—round, square, and rectangular. This was all right for day-to-day use, but when Thanksgiving came and the children began to yell for turkey and mince pie, I found myself in trouble. I had to measure the largest of my rectangular corn-bread tins with a ruler and then spend several hours shopping until I could get a turkey just the proper overall length and beam to fit. The mince pie, baked in another tin, was square.

I had barely accustomed myself to the luxury of having the children in school every day when I found the Christmas holidays upon me. Now the house was filled not only with my own children, but with everyone else's. Whenever I went to the icebox, I found Larry passing out snacks to his friends and bragging about what a good cook his old man was. The house echoed to the sound of the Confederate Army on maneuvers. Janie, who took great pride in the fact that she went off to school every day like the older children, tried to re-establish the nursery school in our house over the holidays. She brought all her friends home and conducted classes in drawing and cutting out paper dolls.

"Today, I fink we'll have sumtraction," I heard her say to the class one morning.

"What's that?" one of the children asked in awe.

"Oh, one take away five is four and fings like 'at," she explained.

It was a few days before I caught on to the fact that all the mothers in towns were preserving peace and quiet in their own homes by sending their children over to my place.

Lynn, in her role as peacemaker and spreader of sweetness and light, tried to keep everything on an amicable plane. She patched up the quarrels between Larry and the neighbors and between Janie and her playmates. But she finally overreached herself one day. Looking for new words to conquer with sunshine, she wandered out of the front door one morning with the two kittens in her arms. A few minutes later, I heard her shriek and rushed out to find her standing in front of a neighbor's house, bleeding from a number of scratches on her arms. Lou, the neighbor's gentle old bird dog, was sitting in front of her, regarding the child solicitously.

"What on earth is the matter?" I asked.

"I was trying to get Lou and the kittens to make friends," she sobbed. "And they scratched me."

That called for a trip to the doctor and a lecture to Lynn, defining the limits to which a mediator may prudently go in this world.

My birthday falls just a week before Christmas, and this year, what with everything, I was willing to pass the whole thing over. But December comes in a season of the year when a child's attitude toward a parent undergoes a remarkable change. My children were being so good that it was hard to recognize them and, as part of their efforts in the right direction, they were insisting that I enjoy a happy birthday.

"You've got to have a birthday dinner," Lynn insisted. "You've just got to."

While I was still trying to wriggle out of it, there came a note from my mother, saying that she was mailing me a birthday cake. So, in spite of an allergy to cooking my own birthday dinner, I told the children we would have a small family celebration. I bought a steak for the occasion and the children haunted the village post office as each mail came in, waiting for Mother's cake. On the afternoon of the great day, the last mail was distributed—but there was no cake. The children were quite crestfallen when they came home to break the news. Then they put their heads together and started to plot. After a time, they told me not to worry about the cake—they would fix everything. It was when they started to fix everything, of course, that I really began to worry. But how was I to know that Mother's cake would arrive the next day?

They rushed off to the store and came back a short time later with a package. Then they chased me out of the kitchen. After an hour or so, I was allowed to come in to cook dinner, but I was given strict orders not to look in the cupboard. I found my cookbook opened to a recipe for uncooked frostings, and when I saw a few gobs of sticky purple stuff on the walls, I got the impression that the kids had bought a cake at the store and decorated it with icing, purple in color.

"Oh, well," I told myself, as I cleaned the walls, "it could have been worse. Suppose they had made the cake, too."

So I cooked the vegetables and broiled the steak for my birthday dinner. Then, putting the things on the table, I called the children to eat. When they reached the kitchen, Larry was seized with a new idea and I was requested to leave the room for a minute.

"Don't let the cats steal the meat," I pleaded.

They called me back a few seconds later and issued a mysterious injunction against opening the oven door. We had a happy dinner and the children were bursting with excitement over the great surprise which awaited me. They cleared off the dinner dishes and then turned out the lights. I heard the oven door open and then a match was struck. There followed three groans of intense anguish, followed by much whispering. Then the electric light was switched back on and the kids approached the table, each with a hand on the cake plate, singing "Happy Birthday, Dear Daddy."

I was very touched as they put their masterpiece in front of me. After taking one look at it I tried to freeze my countenance in the misty-eyed, blissful expression I had been wearing.

"Oh," I exclaimed. "How pretty. Purple *and* yellow icing."

"Just uh purple is icin', Daddy," said Janie by way of correction.

"Something went wrong," Larry explained.

[76]

"You see, we thought it would be nice if we warmed **the** cake up a little," Lynn said.

"So, after you finished broiling the steak, we put it in the oven," said Larry.

"'At yellow is candles melted," said Janie.

"It's very pretty," I said gravely. "I thought you had made it that way on purpose."

"Do you really like it?" Lynn asked excitedly.

"It's the prettiest cake I ever saw," I assured them.

The melted candles and the melted icing by now had blended together beyond any hope of extrication. So, while the children beamed happily, I cut the cake and served it.

It's the only time I remember eating candle wax with any real relish.

Chapter Eight

S INCE we had settled in the Florida cottage, my friend John had been bustling in and out of our life like a small tornado. About once a week, he would make a date to go fishing with me. He never showed up and, finally, I stopped expecting him. Then he did come one day, at the appointed hour, and I wasn't home. I knew he had been there, because I found a pail of dead minnows.

He was in the habit of dropping by at eleven o'clock at night to invite me to go to a party with him, and he always seemed surprised when I reminded him that I couldn't leave the children. Then there came a period when he would bring his parties with him when he called. One morning, about four o'clock, I heard a car pull up in the yard.

"John, that man isn't going to want to see us now. Let's go home," a voice said.

"Listen, he's a good old friend of mine," I heard John insist. "He's a good fellow. He'll be glad to see us."

I lay in bed shuddering, while the argument raged. Then the bedroom door opened and John called me.

"Go away," I mumbled sleepily.

John was silent. Then I heard the door close and John walked back to his car.

"He was asleep," he informed his friends, hurt and surprise mingling in his voice, and they drove away.

I now found myself faced with the necessity of providing Christmas for three children, and that is a prospect which can make even the stoutest male tremble with fear. In our village, there was no place to buy Christmas presents or decorations. We lived twenty miles from the nearest shopping center and I had no car. Good old John told me not to worry, because he would drive out and take us to town to do our shopping. He failed to show up entirely the first three times he made dates with us. The fourth time, he arrived just as I was getting breakfast for the children.

"I didn't expect you so early," I said. "We won't be ready to leave for a while."

"That's all right," he said. "I haven't been to bed yet. Big party. I'll take a little nap while you're getting ready."

I tried to wake him up at twelve, one, and two o'clock. By three o'clock I would have called the coroner, if John hadn't been snoring so vigorously. I bought a couple of extra chops at the country store, on the theory that he might wake up in time for dinner. He did regain consciousness at five-thirty and then rushed off to keep a luncheon date. He was back at midnight, with a small party of twelve. I locked him in the house all night and so we were able to get to town the next day.

By then, there was less than a week until Christmas. I was able to buy some presents for the children but couldn't find a single Christmas tree ornament. Not a piece of tinsel. Not a colored light. Not an icicle. At home, feeling very depressed,

I began to sell the children on the idea of an old-fashioned tree, decorated with crepe paper and colored popcorn. John promised to come back on Christmas Eve to take us out to cut a tree.

"Don't worry about anything," he told me grandly. "I'll take care of everything."

"That," I said sadly, "is just what's worrying me."

"You come to my house for Christmas dinner," John said. "I'd like us all to be together for the day."

"You better not forget to come out here on Christmas Eve to help us get our tree," I said, "or there'll be a murder."

The lack of decorations didn't seem to bother the children. They went ahead gaily, making paper ornaments and dyeing popcorn to string on the tree. Janie was greatly impressed by a street-corner Santa Claus she had seen in town.

"He had a mustache all over his face," I heard her tell one of her friends.

On Christmas Eve, I waited until an hour before sundown and, having decided by then that John had confused this with some other day, I set out to see what I could do without him. There was no axe on our place, but I found a dull old hand saw and started down the road to find a tree. I was feeling so low that I thought I really should travel on all fours. Here it was, Christmas Eve—the most joyous time of the year. And here I was, way off in the wilds of Florida—a poor, lone, incompetent man, completely unversed in all the little niceties that make Christmas such a happy day. I was completely on my own, without a friend in the world, and it was up to me to make Christmas a wonderful thing for three little children. I didn't even have a tree. And, if I did find one, I didn't have any proper decorations to put on it. Yes sir, I certainly was feeling sorry for myself.

In a field of brush and scrub pine I searched until I found a small tree. It wasn't really what I wanted, but it would have to do. With my dull saw, I hacked away for half an hour until I got the little tree down and then I dragged it along toward home. It was a half-mile walk and the sun had set before I reached the house. As I turned the corner, I saw John's car. The door was open and he was unloading a great armload of boxes.

"A fine guy . . ." I started to say.

"What's the matter?" he asked in surprise. "I told you I'd take care of everything."

"A fine time . . ."

"Oh, you *got* the tree," he said happily. "Swell. We can start decorating it."

"We could, if we had some decorations," I said.

"I told you," he said. "I got everything. *Everything.* Nettie McKay decided she wouldn't have a tree this year and she sent all their decorations down for you. Lights and everything. I told you."

I looked at the boxes he was unloading.

"Presents for the kids from everybody in town," he continued. "Nettie and Betty and Freddie and Henry. Everybody. Come on and help me."

"John," I said, as I picked up a load of bundles, "the trouble with you is that I can't even depend on you to be undependable."

He gave me a blank look.

"Your family sent Larry a beagle puppy," he whispered. "I picked it up at the express office and it's in my garage. You can give it to him tomorrow when you come over."

By this time, I was close to being overwhelmed. The poor, lone, helpless male who had dragged down that lonesome road in search of a Christmas tree an hour before was suddenly transformed. He was now a heroic figure, supported by friends and relatives.

We set up the tree and arranged the packages. Then John remembered that he'd promised to go to a party which had started five hours earlier and he began to warm up for a take-off.

"Hey, what about tomorrow?" I asked.

"I'll be down for you first thing in the morning," he said.

"That I doubt. But what about dinner. Have you bought some food?"

"Sure. Nettie bought a chicken for me today. Have you ever cooked a chicken?"

"Hundreds of them!" I retorted. "And by the way, have you got any more knives, yet?"

He snapped his fingers.

"By gosh, I'd forgotten. But I'll borrow some silver tonight."

When I was ready for bed that night, I took a last look at the tree and the presents stacked around it. I was suddenly overwhelmed by the thought of all of the kindness that had made it possible. Yes sir, there is a Santa Claus.

I had hardly gone to sleep when the children were poking me in the ribs to ask whether it was time to get up and open the presents. I made them stay in bed until the sun came up, but that was the best I could do. About nine o'clock I was surprised to see John's car pull up in front of the house. I began to understand this near-miracle when I saw that it was not John, but a friend of his, who was driving the car.

"John couldn't quite make it this morning," the friend explained. "So he asked me to pick you up."

I was able to pry the children loose from the tree, on the

promise of more and better things to come, and we drove to John's house. We got him out of bed and he led us to the garage, where I could hear a familiar sound. John unlocked the door and a six-weeks-old beagle puppy, consisting almost entirely of ears, waddled out toward us, blinking at the light. Larry fell down on his knees, like an Aztec Indian at the first sight of a Conquistador. Lynn and Janie started giving off little girls' squeals of delight.

"What are you going to name him?" I asked Larry, "Jefferson Davis?"

"Tonker," he replied without hesitation. "Remember, we're going to name them all with 'T' after Tinker?"

He started racing toward the house with the dog chasing him and the rest of us following.

The three children spent the next half hour chasing the puppy, or the puppy chasing them, through the front room.

"Look, Daddy, he comes when I whistle 'Dixie,'" Larry cried in glee.

The puppy's yipping and the children's whooping created the kind of bedlam to which I had long since grown accustomed. But I could see a pained look on John's face and I realized that this was not at all the way he had expected that Christmas would be.

The puppy paused for a few seconds in the middle of the room and the inevitable happened.

"Uh, oh," said Janie. "'E's sprung uh leak."

I hastened for a rag.

"Got some company coming," John said a few minutes later.

"What time shall we have dinner, then?" I asked.

"Oh, about two or three o'clock," he suggested.

"Then I'll start the chicken cooking about one," I said. "What vegetable did you get?"

"I got some frozen peas," he replied. "And I got a pressure cooker for Christmas. Did you ever work one?"

"Nope," I said.

"It's simple," he assured me. "There are some directions with it and they look easy. Only takes a minute or so to cook up the peas."

By now, Larry and Janie had fallen to arguing about whose turn it was to pet the puppy. Lynn was trying to adjudicate the matter by suggesting that one pet him on the head and the other on the tail. That stopped them for a minute, but then they began to quarrel about who was to pet the head first. By the time the exasperated Lynn had settled this, the puppy had gone out to John's room, where he found a hand-painted necktie to chew on.

A short time after this, I went out to the kitchen to get the chicken ready for the oven. I had started to make the stuffing and was getting along fine when John suddenly remembered that he'd promised some friends down the road to bring us over for breakfast.

"Oh, John," I protested, "breakfast's finished hours ago. Dinner's cooking now."

"We gotta go," he insisted. "We'll be gone for just a few minutes."

"Let me get the chicken started," I pleaded. "Or else we'll never have dinner."

"You're getting just like a woman," he complained. "Stop worrying about your dinner and come on. We will be right back."

So I left the chicken and we went along with John. Break-

[84]

fast, of course, had long since disappeared from our host's table, but it had been replaced by a large bowl of eggnog—from which it was difficult to separate friend John. By the time we got back to his house, we knew that our dinner was going to be good and late. I worked on the chicken as fast as I could, but I hadn't quite put it in the oven when company arrived and John insisted that I leave the kitchen to entertain his friends while he went down the road to borrow some knives.

It was half an hour before he got back, and I finally put the chicken in the oven at the hour when I had originally intended to serve dinner. The company left at last, so I gave the children some sandwiches and milk to tide them over and went out to the kitchen to put together a mince pie. It took me well over an hour, because more company kept arriving and John would come out to the kitchen and order me to wash the dough off my hands and come out to meet the new arrivals.

"Al's cooking dinner for us," John would explain.

This remark always brought snickers from the women, and then John insisted upon describing my talents as a cook and the women had to ask questions to see whether I really knew what I was doing. This kept me away from my duties for another fifteen minutes, every time it happened, and I was slowly going crazy. I now estimated that the chicken would be ready to come out of the oven about five o'clock but, since the peas didn't take but one minute in the wonderful pressure cooker, I wasn't worried about getting them ready in advance. During a lull in the festivities, I managed to peel some potatoes and I put them on to boil. It was getting late in the afternoon and normal people had finished their Christmas dinners and were going calling. So John's living room continued to seat a capacity crowd.

About five-fifteen, I was fretting over my dinner in the

kitchen, when I noticed that a strange quiet had fallen over the house. I peeked out into the living room to see that all the guests had disappeared. The little girl had fallen asleep on a chair in the corner, with the exhausted puppy on her lap. Lynn was playing jacks on the front stoop, and Larry, who had been badgering John's guests all afternoon, was sitting quietly, reading *The Public Papers of Franklin D. Roosevelt.*

"Good night," I said to John. "I thought you'd never get rid of those people. Let's for heaven's sake have dinner."

"You don't know how I've been looking forward to this dinner," he said.

John had me put up a card table in the living room. I had the girls set the table. I was just ready to take the chicken out of the oven when the door opened and the night shift of company came in.

"What'll I do?" I complained to John. "Everything's going to be ruined. The children are starved."

"They won't stay but a minute," he assured me in a whisper.

The minute grew into half an hour. During that time, Larry interrupted the general conversation fourteen times with questions relating to President Roosevelt's First Inauguration; Lynn brought into the living room a turtle which she had found in the yard and wept bitterly when John threatened to make it into soup; and Janie cut her finger on a piece of broken glass. I would sneak out into the kitchen every few minutes to baste the chicken and stir the potatoes, which were warming on a back burner. But still the guests showed no signs of battle fatigue.

I had already made a meal off my fingernails, but I was trying to save some food for the rest of them. The pie was cooked, although it had taken twice as long as any pie I had ever seen. The bird was as brown as a fallen leaf, so I turned the dial on the electric oven down low. Suddenly, Larry appeared in the kitchen.

"Hey, when do we eat?" he demanded.

"Sh! Sh!" I said. "There's company out there."

"Oh, they've gone," he said. "Let's eat."

I looked into the living room and it was empty, all right. John walked back in the door, rubbing his hands in anticipation.

"Gosh, you don't know how I've been looking forward to this," he said.

There was something so wistful about his tone that I stifled any retort which might have come to mind and set about mashing the potatoes and making the gravy.

"It'll be ready in just a couple of minutes, if this pressure cooker works," I said. "Lynn, you help me get the things on the table."

John went back to the living room and I sent the girls out with bread and butter and other incidentals. They were putting on the celery and cranberry sauce when I heard the sound of new, strange voices.

"Wait a minute," I called to the girls.

Looking in the living room, I saw a fresh supply of company there. I went in to greet them and then dragged John out to the kitchen.

"I've *got* to feed these children," I said frantically. "What'll I do?"

"These people will go in just a few minutes," he said. "I do *so* want to have Christmas dinner with you and your family."

Again, it was that wistful tone that got me. I went back into the living room and sat down, having shoved the chicken back in the oven and restored the potatoes to the back burner. Larry started reading excerpts from Roosevelt's Second Inaugural

Address at the top of his lungs and the company said what a remarkable boy. For the first five minutes of it, that is. Then I had to chase the kid out of the room. Some twenty minutes later, the company rose to depart and I hustled back into the kitchen. But, just as the chicken came out of the oven, four more people arrived. As soon as I could, I got John out of the living room.

"Old man," I said quietly but firmly, "I love you like a brother and I wish with all my heart that we could all sit down to Christmas dinner together. But if I don't feed those children right away, they are going to start showing the effects of malnutrition."

"Oh, just wait a little longer . . ."

"Absolutely not. I'll feed them out here in the kitchen."

So I sent Lynn out to clear the things off the table. The celery, it developed, had been consumed by a hungry visitor. I finished making the gravy and then set the pressure cooker into operation. After it had spit and snarled for a spell, I decided that the peas must be done and I put them aside. At this point, John called me into the living room to meet someone who had just arrived. When I got back, my potatoes had burned.

"Oh well," I told the children, "you've got to expect these things around here."

I chucked the potatoes in the garbage, set the chicken down on the table and dumped the peas in the serving dish. The sound they made—like ball bearings dropping on concrete— should have warned me, but I was too harassed to pay attention. I got the children to sit down, took a look at their happy faces, and started to carve the chicken. When I applied the knife gently, it made no impression.

"Dull knife," I said, bearing down harder.

Still, nothing happened. I sharpened the knife and went back

[88]

to the attack. Finally, I made an incision, but what I saw when I succeeded in parting the leg bone from the carcass caused me to grip the table to steady myself. For the bird was running red. The skin was nice and brown and the fowl had stayed in the oven, one way or another, for at least an extra hour. Still, it obviously wasn't done.

"Oh well," I told the children. "We still have peas and gravy."

I suddenly remembered the noise the peas had made and decided to sample one. In doing this, I almost broke a tooth—the pressure cooker hadn't even thawed them out. I decided I had better read the cooker directions again.

"Oh well," I said to the children, "at least we've got the gravy."

Nothing was wrong with the gravy and the children had just begun to eat their Christmas dinner, consisting of bread with gravy on it, when John appeared in the kitchen.

"I got rid of everyone, finally," he said happily. "Now, let's eat."

"John," I said, "there's something I've got to tell you."

He looked at me, puzzled.

"The chicken didn't get cooked. The potatoes got burned. And the peas are hard as pebbles."

He was unimpressed by my complaints against equipment and working conditions.

"I thought you said you could cook," he replied, looking at me in disgust.

A few minutes later, John opened the oven door to peek at the chicken. Suddenly, he straightened up and snapped his fingers.

"Golly, I meant to get that fixed," he said.

"What's that?"

"The oven's been going haywire. The broiler's the only thing you can really count on."

"Possibly," I suggested, "that's why the chicken didn't get roasted."

"I'm sorry," John said contritely, but then he started to laugh uproariously. "What'll we do?"

"Do you know how to commit hari-kiri?" I suggested.

"Wait—" he said happily. "Let's put the chicken in the pressure cooker. I'll see how long it takes."

He started to thumb through his book of instructions and finally said:

"Here it is—'Chicken—ten minutes.'"

"We'll give it fifteen," I said. "I don't think this chicken wants to be cooked."

We stuffed the chicken in the cooker and after fifteen minutes of hissing and sputtering, John urged me to take it off the fire. We fished the bird out of the cooker. It looked like nothing so much as a tired old inner tube. I tried the knife on it, but I couldn't even make a dent in the skin.

"I give up," I announced. "Where's the nearest hamburger stand?"

"Look," John said earnestly. "I promised Nettie that we'd bring the kids by to see her. Let's go down to her house and she'll have some cold turkey they can eat. I'll tell her that this chicken she got is no good."

"Okay," I said dubiously.

Nettie met us at the door and led us to the living room.

"Well," she asked pleasantly as we settled down. "How were the chicken and dumplings?"

"Dumplings?" I asked. "Dumplings with roast chicken?"

"*Roast* chicken?" she asked in surprise.

"Oh," said John, snapping his fingers again, "I forgot to tell you, Al, I wanted you to make some dumplings. I love chicken and dumplings."

"But, John," I said, "dumplings go with *stewed* chicken."

"And that *was* a stewing chicken I bought for you," said Nettie. "That's what you wanted."

"Is there any difference?" my friend John asked, in surprise. "It's all chicken, isn't it?"

"The main difference is that you can't roast a stewing chicken, as you could plainly see," I said, a little bitterly. "And especially you can't bake one in a broken oven."

"Well, why didn't it cook in the pressure cooker?" John demanded. "I know you can make chicken and dumplings in a pressure cooker."

"How much time did you give it?" Nettie asked suspiciously.

"The book said ten minutes," said John. "So we gave it fifteen and still it didn't get cooked."

"That's ten minutes *to the pound!*" Nettie shrieked. "That bird weighed about six pounds."

"I'm hungry," said Janie.

"Me, too," said Larry.

"I don't wonder," said our hostess. "Come on, we've got a lot of cold turkey in the kitchen."

She bustled out toward the kitchen.

"*Men,*" she said, shaking her head slowly. "Men."

"*Some* men," I said, by way of amendment.

Chapter Nine

NEW YEAR'S morning was dull and foggy when I looked upon it—in spite of the fact that the Florida sun was shining its brightest. We had accepted John's invitation to spend New Year's Eve at his house. But of course there weren't enough beds to go around. In his exuberance, John had invited two other friends to spend the night. One, a magazine editor from New York, was farmed out, lucky fellow, for the sleeping part of the night with a neighbor. The other guest was a young man named Rodney, who was riding around the state on a motorcycle collecting snakes, a couple of which he had crawling over him at all times. The neighbor who put up the magazine editor offered to take in the snake collector, without his snakes.

"Don't worry about me," Rodney said. "I've got a sleeping bag and I'll just curl up out in the yard. If you'll keep the snakes in the house, that is, so they won't get away."

"But suppose it rains?" John asked.

"That's all right. My sleeping bag is waterproof."

I could see that this piece of information intrigued the children. Janie wanted to know what would happen if it snowed. This suggested an interminable list of questions to Larry, such

[92]

as what would happen if you slept in a mud puddle, what would happen if you took a shower with the sleeping bag on, and what would happen if you fell out of a canoe while wearing the sleeping bag. Having exhausted every possibility on the subject, he said at last:

"Gee, I hope it rains. I'd like to find out how the darn thing works."

I let Larry and Lynn stay up to see the New Year in. The little one protested that she, too, wanted to see it come in, but when I explained that it did not, as she had supposed, come down the chimney like Santa Claus, she decided to go to bed. I tried to impress upon the children the need for sleeping late the next morning—not only for their own welfare, but also out of consideration for John. The children understood perfectly, but I forgot to speak to the puppy. So he awoke at his normal hour and, by six o'clock, he had the children out of bed. They dressed quietly and had some cereal. By then, it was six thirty, and the prospects of entertainment, with all the grownups sleeping so late, were rather dim. John and I were doing our snoring indoors, while Rodney was sleeping at the foot of an old oak tree. Actually I, at least, was half awake but playing possum upon the crack of dawn.

Lynn remembered Rodney's snakes, which had been put away in a box for the night; she decided that it would be a good idea if Tonker and the reptiles made friends. So she let the snakes out and the puppy had a fine time, for a little while, yapping at them. After a bit, this became boring to the children and so they decided to eat some more cereal. Then Larry remembered the alligator farm down the road and the three of them set off. They took Tonker, but left the snakes behind because they couldn't find them. Lynn was very disappointed

[93]

about this; she wanted to see if the snakes and the alligators would make friends.

At the alligator farm, the children woke up the reptilian inmates and, eventually, the proprietors of the establishment. They, too, had stayed up late the night before, figuring that no one would be paying to see reptiles on New Year's morning. After getting chased out of there, the children wandered back to the house. They saw Rodney in his sleeping bag.

"Heck, it didn't rain," Lynn said.

"I wonder if that thing really is waterproof," Larry speculated.

"Look," cried Janie, "'Ere's a big snake."

It wasn't really a big snake, but in the hands of those three children it was something nearly as lethal. It was a garden hose. Larry's glance ran from the hose to the sleeping bag and then the great idea hit him. It was a few minutes later that certain sounds began to penetrate my consciousness.

"Huh, it wasn't waterproof at all," I heard Larry yell derisively.

"The sleeping bag is waterproof, but my face isn't, you little monsters," I heard Rodney cry. He was hopping around the yard, water dripping from his head, and madder than a funny-paper character.

"Look, it's raining," Larry yelled. Then I heard the girls' screams followed by the sound of slamming doors. I braced myself as the two girls burst into the bedroom which John and I were occupying.

"Daddy, Daddy," Janie was yelling.

"Look what Larry's done," said Lynn.

With half-opened eyes, I looked at the two drenched girls who were standing at the foot of the bed. Before I could get my eyes completely open, Larry had wheeled the artillery up to the open window and let fly with another salvo, just for good measure. I was hit in the face by a spray of cold water.

"Cut it out!" I yelled.

At this moment, John sat up in bed abruptly. He let out a hoarse yell and dove back under the covers. It was easy to figure out why he had done this, because when he had sat up, he had come face to face with the two fugitive snakes, coiled up on the foot of his bed!

"Oh, there you are," said Lynn happily, as she saw the snakes. "I've been looking all over for you bad little girls."

She started to pick up the snakes and they started for my bed. I started for the door, yelling for Rodney. We collided head on, just outside the door.

"Where's my snakes?" Rodney demanded indignantly.

"They went that-a-way," I said, picking myself up and continuing this-a-way.

It was fifteen minutes before order was restored. I put the girls back to bed and hung out their clothes to dry. Larry had taken off for parts unknown, so a three-man reception committee sat down to await his return.

"I don't really mind the water in my face," said Rodney, tactfully, "But he shouldn't have put that bow tie around the snake. Might have choked him."

"Did you ever wake up on New Year's and find a snake with a polka-dot tie staring you in the face?" John said plaintively. "Al, I swear, I love those kids as if they were my own, but you've got to do something about them. They're certainly running all over you."

This was an opinion which had been expressed, with perhaps less directness, on a number of occasions recently, and so I was

[95]

now willing to take it with a certain amount of seriousness. Conceding that the children were slightly less inhibited and disciplined than they should have been, my problem was what to do about it. A few days later, I was talking with Larry's teacher, who implied that it was because of boys like him that there was a shortage of teachers.

"I do my best to keep him under control," I said sadly. "I don't know what you'd suggest."

"Well, some parents give their children a little dash of the willow switch," she said sharply. "You're bigger than he is."

"I'm not much for whipping children," I said. "I don't think it gets you anywhere."

"*Well!*" she said, in a tone that took care of that.

Soon after this, a friend dropped in and mentioned a book on child psychology. I arranged to borrow it immediately. The book set forth the thesis that children should be rewarded for good behavior, rather than being punished for misdeeds. Without a moment's hesitation I bought this idea and set my fuzzy brain to work on a plan to carry it out. For some time, the two older children had been begging me to buy them bicycles. That should be bait enough for a lot of good conduct, I thought.

"We're going to start something new," I told the children. "How'd you like to earn a couple of bicycles?"

The response was enthusiastic, so I went on to outline my plan.

"I've fixed up a chart," I said. "And you'll see things like Courtesy, Helpfulness, School, and so forth written down on it. Now, every day I'm going to give you a grade on these things, based on how well you behave and how you do your household chores around here. You'll get a mark on them at the end of the week and I'll give you a pay check, depending upon your grades.

When you get enough money in pay checks, we can buy the bikes."

"How long will it take?" Larry asked suspiciously.

"Well, if you get a perfect score, you make $2.50 a week toward the bikes."

He did some quick figuring.

"Gosh, you mean we can't get them for about twenty weeks?"

"That's not long, Larry," said Lynn.

"Not long! Gosh!" he said. "Couldn't you let us have the money now, and then, when we get the bikes, we could earn it?"

As part of the new system, I gave the children a list of chores. They had dishes to wash and dry, beds to make, clothes to pick up, and, on Saturdays, they were given a few hours of extra duty. In this way, I hoped to get rid of part of the housework and at the same time by keeping them busy, allow myself more time for writing.

On the first day, Lynn came home from school to wash the dishes. I heard her in the kitchen rattling glass and china around for an hour or so. Finally I wandered out to see why it was taking her so long. She was gazing out of the window when I entered.

"Gee, these glasses were dirty, Daddy," she said. "I had to use soap and wash them about five times. I ought to get a good mark for Thoroughness."

I looked and saw that the time she had been working, she had managed to wash and dry, to sparkling perfection, a total of six glasses. The rest of the dishes still were waiting to be done. But I said nothing. "Don't Criticize," the psychology book had warned me. When Larry discovered that it had taken Lynn two hours to wash and dry the dishes, he burst into loud guffaws.

"I can do them in five minutes," he boasted.

[98]

"You can not," she said.

The next day, he did them in four minutes, storming into the house and out again before I knew he had even started. When I looked over the dishes, I was surprised that it had taken him that long. Apparently he had just dusted them off lightly with the dish rag. So I set them aside and the next time he popped into the house I told him ever so politely, but ever so firmly, that he'd have to do them again.

Against Larry's speed, Lynn retaliated by bringing home a couple of playmates to help her with the work. They were glad to oblige: it let them out of having to do the same thing at home. It got so that Lynn would bring six girls home with her every afternoon, and they were playing "you-be-the-momma-and-I'll-be-the-Daddy" with so much attendant noise that I couldn't write a line. So I had to limit her to two helpers per day.

The pay checks were rather meager the first week, and when the children saw that they'd really have to work in order to earn the money, they began to take the idea more seriously. Larry again complained that it would require so long to earn the bikes that he'd be wanting an automobile instead. This was all right with me, because I was looking forward to months of comparative peace and quiet. But I didn't want to lower his morale, so I cast about for some new incentive.

"I tell you what I'll do," I said. "You kids haven't been getting such good marks in school. So, for every 'A' on your report cards, I'll add five dollars to the bicycle fund."

That seemed to satisfy them and I knew that, as things stood, I was running only a small risk. For A's on their report cards were few and far between. This was not entirely their fault; largely it was the result of a local situation. When we moved to the village, I had become friendly with some people in our block. As time went by, I found out that they were all active participants in a minor civil war which was raging in the town.

The war was being fought over the competency of one of the teachers in the two-room school, and no one in town was permitted to remain neutral on the subject. My friends were solidly against the teacher and, while I didn't have any feelings on the matter myself, I discovered that the teacher's supporters already considered me their enemy. As an outsider, it was impossible for me to comprehend the deadly seriousness with which these southerners were conducting their feud.

I wasn't even aware of how deeply I was involved in it until the children brought home their first report cards. These showed low marks in reading and spelling—subjects in which I knew they excelled. I mentioned this to one of my local friends and she explained readily:

"It's because you're a friend of mine. She hates me so that she would do anything."

I found this incredible, but inquiry showed that everyone on the anti-teacher side of the war expected their children to get low marks. So, I let it go at that, having satisfied myself that the children were really doing their work and learning the things that they should know. But, when I made the offer of five dollars for each 'A,' I did it with tongue in cheek.

About this time, I added a new feature to our program for the more abundant family life. Each day, I allowed one of the children to choose the menu for the evening meal. This child would also select a topic or two for dinner-table conversation and would lead the discussion. This system gave the children a chance to pick out those dishes they liked best and kept conversation above the "Yah, yah, you're another" level.

To earn the right to order a meal, a child had to eat without

[100]

protest the food chosen by the others. To make sure no important items were dropped from our diet, I selected every fourth meal myself. The older children displayed a certain amount of imagination as menu inventors, but it proved necessary for me to offer Janie a good bit of help and guidance. When it was her turn to order her first meal, I asked what she wanted.

"Noodles, an' choc'lut puddin' for berserk," she said firmly.

"And what else?" I asked.

"'At's all."

"But don't you want some meat and a vegetable?"

"Nope."

"Well, you let me pick those out for you. I'll get something you like. Now what are you going to talk about at dinner?"

"Jus' dolls."

"What about them?"

"Tweenie's been sick wif chick'pox. I wanta talk about 'at."

That was about as far as I ever got with her, either in meal planning or conversation. Her horizon was limited to noodles, chocolate puddings, and the life and times of her dolls named Tweenie.

By now I was holding a commanding lead over the children. I had finished two-thirds of my winter's writing schedule, while they had earned one-third of their bicycle money, when our town was split at the seams by The Big Explosion. I heard my first report of it one afternoon when the children came home from school and mentioned casually that after school hours the teacher, in a fit of anger, had slapped a child named Joan. This information made no great impression upon me immediately, because the teacher was in the habit of rapping knuckles or warming the seat of someone's pants—usually Larry's. But it seemed that slapping a child in anger, after school hours, constituted a major offense, and within half an hour, I sensed that something truly cataclysmic had happened. Neighbors began dashing wildly into our house and asking:

"Did you hear?"

Little clusters of citizens gathered on the corners, glowering at one another. When I walked to the post office late in the afternoon, two women with whom I had a nodding acquaintance turned up their noses at me when I spoke to them. And when I got to the store, I found people with red, angry faces discussing the slapping incident.

"Wait until Joan's daddy gets home."

"I heard that his wife had called him up in Jacksonville and told him to get right back."

During the next few days, developments came thick and fast. The warring citizens established headquarters in the two grocery stores and you could enter enemy territory to buy a can of coffee only at the risk of being accused of espionage. Excited female couriers dashed up and down the village, broadcasting the latest news bulletins. Flash!!!—Joan's father confronts teacher. Terrible scene follows. Teacher stands on rights. More scenes. Teacher admits her "hand slipped" after Joan sassed her. Joan's father demands apology. Teacher orders him off school property. Joan's father to hire lawyer. Flash!!!—Teacher apologizes to Joan's father. Teacher informed that Joan's mother had been raising questions about her morals and demands apology. Apology insufficient for some citizens—they notify county superintendent of education. Petition circulates demanding removal of teacher. Rumor that state superintendent of education may be called in. Perhaps governor.

Everyone in town was very busy and, as far as I could make out, very happy about the whole thing. Except me. I had passed the teacher on the street and she had hurriedly looked the other way. I knew that I was truly condemned in her eyes and I began to worry about my poor little children. Then the people who were still speaking to me announced that the district school board was going to hold a hearing on the question of the teacher's competence. Everyone was going to be there and that, it developed, included me. Someone would pick me up at eight o'clock and they had arranged for a high-school girl to watch the children while I was gone.

The meeting was held in the local high school, with the teacher sitting with her friends on one side of the room. When I walked in with my friends I found that we were supposed to sit on the opposite side and glower at the other crowd. The three members of the school board were red-necked Florida crackers who seemed mightily confused by the whole thing. When they called the meeting to order, everyone tried to talk at once. I assumed that there would be some orderly calling of witnesses, but such was not to be the case.

"I reckon," said the school board chairman, "that there ain't nothing for us to do but let ever'body in the room get up and speak his piece. Now, what's all this trouble about?"

Everyone began to babble again. People on my side of the room were shaking their fists and shouting at people on the other side of the room. The teacher, flushed and nervous, kept glowering at me as if I were to blame for the whole thing. Actually, I had no personal quarrel with her and the whole situation made me so uncomfortable that I just wanted to turn myself inside out. Finally, the chairman restored order and called on the mother of the slapped child to voice her complaint.

"It's a lie," the teacher kept crying out, as the story unfolded. "It's a dirty lie!"

Joan's mother had barely finished when another mother leaped to her feet.

"And I aim to tell what that woman did to my little Bill," she shrieked. "Just because he didn't know his spelling lesson, she took his lunch away from him and dropped it in the wastebasket and that poor child didn't have a blessed thing to eat the live-long day and come home that night to his mother so hungry he was crying."

"It's a lie," shouted the teacher. "All that poor child had for lunch was some spoiled meat! Why, I love that boy just like one of my own. Many's the day I've shared my lunch with him. Many's the day I've given him the love and the kindness he should be getting from his mother."

"That's a lie," shouted Billy's mother.

"Sit down, Honey," said Billy's father as he arose to speak. "If you were a man," he addressed the teacher, "I'd take you outside and beat you for what you just said. And if there's a man here who will stand up for you, I'll take *him* outside."

There was a moment of silence while everyone waited to see whether there was indeed a man to step outside with Billy's father. Personally, I considered it the best offer I'd heard all evening and was seriously considering accepting it myself, just as a means of getting out of the place.

But suddenly a woman who was sitting near the teacher cried out: "Let us pray." She bowed her head and began: "The Lord is my shepherd . . ."

"The prayers of the wicked availeth nought," shouted someone on our side.

"Let him who is without sin cast the first stone," snapped back someone on the other side.

[104]

". . . beside still waters . . ." the praying woman continued.

At this point, I was carefully studying the path to the only
exit from the room. Unfortunately, I had picked a seat from
which it was impossible to move without disturbing everyone.
So I shrank down in my chair and futilely tried to recall a suitable
Biblical quotation.

"If you'd only read your Bible," an elderly man on the teacher's side was saying now, "you wouldn't bear such malice in your
hearts. Why, I'll bet that among you poor sinners there's not one
of you who can quote a single chapter out of the Good Book!"

"Thou hypocrite, first cast the beam out of thine own eye,"
a red-faced man roared from our side. "When did *you* start living by the Bible?"

"Judge not, that ye be not judged," the teacher urged.

The chairman of the meeting finally succeeded in restoring
some semblance of order and the testimony for and against the
teacher resumed. Everyone at the meeting was expected to voice
an opinion—the idea that anyone could be neutral on the subject
of the teacher was inconceivable. I squirmed down deeper
and deeper in my chair, hoping that the chairman wouldn't
see me. As the evening wore on, the teacher began to emerge
in the testimony as a most puzzling character. One set of witnesses pictured her as a woman of violent temper, questionable
morals, low intelligence, and, possibly, a secret drinker. The
other group held her up as the soul of patience, a Bible student,
a brilliant molder of character, and an absolute teetotaler. Then
I found that my passionate desire for anonymity was not to be
granted.

"The brother in the rear, there," I heard the chairman say,
"the stout genn'man. What's he have to say?"

[105]

Rising to my feet, I felt about as much at ease as if I had suddenly discovered that my clothes had all fallen off.

"I came not to bear witness," I said, hoping it would sound like a Biblical allusion. "I've lived here such a short time that I don't think I should offer an opinion on this matter. I just came to hear what the others had to say."

"He's not a southerner," the teacher stage-whispered to a neighbor, "but he's the only gentleman on that side of the room."

About ten days later I heard the sound of running feet on the street. At first I thought it was some new manifestation of the local feud, perhaps a lynching bee. So I looked out of the window casually to see if the victim were anyone of my acquaintance. What I saw was an army of children, evidently just turned out of school. The first four feet belonged to Larry and Lynn and they burst in the door immediately. Ten or fifteen of their friends stampeded in after them.

"Daddy! Daddy! We got our report cards!" they yelled.

"Well, what's all the excitement? What's all the mob here for?" I asked.

"They want to see your face when you look at the reports," Larry explained.

"Okay," I said uneasily. "Let's have a look."

"Here, first read this note from the teacher," said Lynn. "She said it was very important."

I opened the envelope and read:

"There has been some talk about favoritism in giving out marks. I certainly do not think you have any grounds for complaints, since I have tried to be very fair in grading your children."

I glanced around the room at the circle of eager faces. All eyes were focused on me. I resolved that, no matter what the cryptic note from the teacher meant, I would not move a facial muscle. Slowly, I opened Larry's report card. Then, frantically, I opened Lynn's. By the time I had studied them both, I had forgotten about my facial muscles and a roar of delight went up from the crowd.

"That's fine," I gulped, trying to regain my composure.

"All 'A's' on both of them," Lynn cried.

"That's thirty-five dollars you owe us both," Larry yelled.

"That's enough so we can get the bikes," Lynn whooped.

"No more courtesy. No more work!" cried Larry.

"And no more writing," I moaned.

Then there was a sudden roaring noise, as of a hurricane striking, and when I looked up, everyone had vanished.

"Hey," I yelled, "somebody come back here and do the dishes!"

But there was no answer, except for the sound of running feet, which grew ever fainter in the distance.

Chapter Ten

IN our village the fount of all wisdom was Buttons, proprietor of one of the local stores. He was a gentle, pleasant man and infinitely accommodating. His insatiable curiosity about the smallest details concerning the lives of the people in town enabled him to build up an inexhaustible store of knowledge about everyone. He was one of the people, yet somehow he remained a little aloof. So many of us owed him bills, or knew we would one day, that Buttons was able to look upon the local scene with the objectivity and realism of a credit manager. And, since he was beholden to no man in town, he could afford to be quite frank in discussing anyone, or anyone's business. Buttons was a friend of everyone—except Old Man Holmes, who had skinned him in a real-estate deal.

On our first day in town, I went to call on Buttons. After introducing myself, I told him where we were living.

"How're you going to keep that place warm?" he asked me immediately.

"Oh," I said casually, "there's a fireplace, if it gets that chilly."

He smiled inscrutably.

"Does it get very cold around here?" I asked, puzzled.

"It gets right cold. Yes, suh."

"Not *really* cold," I insisted.

"Well, suh, we don't very seldom get snow in Florida."

"The landlord told me the fireplace kept that house cozy last winter."

Again, he gave me the inscrutable smile.

"Got any firewood?" he asked.

"No, I haven't."

"I'll get a boy to tote you some."

"I'd certainly appreciate it."

"Too bad my cabins ain't been built," he said sadly. "I'm going to put stove heat in them."

"You're going to build some cabins?" I asked.

He smiled wryly and told me about his feud with Old Man Holmes. It appeared that the old man had owned three lots in one block in town and had sold Buttons two of them, keeping the center lot for himself. Buttons had planned to build cabins on his lots, to rent by the week. But just when he was ready to start them, Old Man Holmes had announced he was going to raise chickens in a weatherbeaten hen house on the center lot.

"You know nobody is going to live in a cabin next to a chicken house," Buttons said bitterly, "so I didn't build them."

"That's too bad," I said. "You'd make a good landlord."

"That old man thinks I'm going to get disgusted and sell the property back to him at half price," Buttons went on as if I hadn't spoken. "But I ain't going to do it."

Every day after that, I went to the store to buy my groceries and gossip with Buttons. My firewood arrived as promised, but since the weather continued balmy, I used to joke with Buttons about the pile of wood. I accused him of victimizing the tourists by frightening them into buying fuel. The children went swimming the day before Christmas, as they had been doing regularly. None of the native children were permitted to go swimming between October and March. This is a mark of the true Floridian, like an aversion to eating citrus fruit.

On New Year's Day, my children were still swimming outdoors. Larry had received a pair of under-water goggles and a flotilla of toy boats for Christmas and was now operating a fleet of sponge boats, for which he acted as chief deep-sea diver. The Confederacy had indeed become the Lost Cause, because its peerless leader had abandoned it completely. The girls were teaching the twelve Tweenies to swim and quite a job it was. Early in January, we had a visit from my younger sister, whom I had not seen in some time. She travels a great deal and had just returned from Latin America. After a few days with us, she headed back to Washington. Since she had extra space in her trunk I shipped the children's winter clothes and our extra blankets back home with her.

A few days after my sister left, it finally got cool enough to give me an excuse to light the fireplace and use up some of my surplus wood. I told Buttons about this and asked him:

"Is this as cold as it gets?"

"No, suh. Gets colder than this."

It warmed up again two days later and the children were able to resume their swimming. After that, it got chilly enough in the evening to justify a fire sometimes and I managed to put a dent in the woodpile.

Early in February, John made one of his never-kept dates to go fishing. The day before he was to come, the weather did something alarming. It got cold. I had to keep the fire going all day and admitted to Buttons that I was glad he had suggested the wood.

"Is this as cold as it gets?" I asked—feeling a little smug, because it really wasn't too bad with the fireplace roaring away in our house.

"No, suh. Radio says it's going to get really chilly tonight. Probably freeze the citrus."

I was still skeptical, but about 3:00 A.M. I awoke shaking like a Model T Ford. Getting up to hunt for extra blankets, I remembered that I had sent all except one of them home with my sister. So I put that on the girls' bed, covered Larry with my raincoat, and donned a sweater to shiver out the rest of the night. I got up early and built a huge fire, but it merely warmed up part of the living room, leaving the rest of the house as cold as a penguin's instep. Then, by turning on all the burners of the kitchen stove, I managed to get the kitchen warm enough to cook breakfast there. The day was gray and windy and a glance at the thermometer on the front porch showed that the temperature had gone down below forty during the night. Certainly John wouldn't keep his fishing date on a day like this. But I should have realized that this was exactly the kind of day when John *would* appear.

He rolled up in front of the house shortly after lunch. He was accompanied by a young lady, a child, and an ancient crone, dressed in a maid's uniform.

"What are we going to do," I asked, "fish through the ice?"

"It's too cold to fish," John replied seriously. "We're going to Orlando and have dinner with some friends of mine."

I was hardly able to start my usual protests against leaving the children, and so on, before John explained that everything was arranged. The maid was to look after all the kids. She

[111]

didn't seem strong enough, but when I saw her bring in a load of firewood that would have staggered a mule I was persuaded otherwise. So we left, spent our afternoon in Orlando, and returned after dinner. All was peaceful and the house seemed singularly warm when we got back, in spite of the fact that the thermometer on the porch was registering thirty-five.

"Have you been cold in here?" I asked the maid.

"No suh, boss. We kep' plenty warm."

The fire died down during the night and I woke up shivering again. Crawling out of bed in the morning, I saw that the fields were covered with a heavy frost. On my way to the woodpile, I looked at the thermometer. It was registering thirty and I saw that there was a skim of ice on the mud puddles. By the time I had reached the woodpile, my blood had begun to freeze a little, too. I understood suddenly how they had been able to keep the house so warm the day before—because there were only three pieces of wood left out of what had been a big pile. I made the best fire that I could, turned on the kitchen stove full blast, and wrapped the children in a blanket. Then I headed for the store and my friend Buttons.

"Gotta have some wood, right away," I told him.

"Well, suh, don't think you're going to get it," he said. "The boy who brought your wood is in jail. And the other fellow who cuts wood was two weeks behind with his orders, *before* this cold started."

I thought for a moment. "Is this as cold as it gets?" I asked uneasily.

"This is pretty cold. Yes, suh."

"But does it get any colder than this?"

"Radio says it'll go down to twenty-two tonight."

[112]

I looked at the gray clouds outside. "If I were up home," I said, "I'd say it looked like snow."

"It don't very seldom snow in Florida," Buttons insisted.

Now having bought my groceries for the day I started home. And I was just turning the corner to my house when I felt a familiar tickle on the end of my nose. Yes, it *was* snow. Just a few little flakes, but it was definitely snow. Within a few minutes, it was coming steadily, mixed with sleet. When I reached the house, I found my children, each dressed in the only two sweaters that I had held out for them, dancing around happily in the front yard.

"Snow," cried Janie happily. "Des like New York."

"Call the janitor," I suggested, "and tell him we want more heat."

The children and I set out to scour the neighborhood for sticks of wood and found enough to keep the fire going until evening. At that time, I went over to the rickety old bookcase and picked out an armload of historical novels someone had sent me. They burned fine. The next morning, I began to relieve the bookcase of its load of old magazines and found that they gave off a certain amount of warmth. It had, indeed, hit twenty-two during the night, and it was now possible for us to stay in the house only if we all crowded on the hearth. I set the card table there, and when it was time for a meal, I put on my raincoat and ran out into the kitchen to cook. I had to keep running all the time I was cooking, to stave off frostbite. We lived on the hearth all day, rationing out the few remaining sticks of wood and the rest of the magazines.

It was about this time that the cock-eyed bookcase, freed of its load of literature, quietly collapsed. It expired with sort of a sigh and, as I looked at the pieces on the floor, I got a

[113]

fiendish idea. Leaving the hearth long enough to break the bookcase into fireplace-sized pieces, I fed the flames for a time longer.

Two kitchen chairs, one with a list to port and the other with a list to starboard, followed the bookcase into the fire. Then went the shelves out of the bedroom closet and a couple of loose boards out of the side of the garage. Finally, I looked at the children hopefully.

"Why don't you collect all those little urchins who usually congregate here," I suggested, "and the whole bunch of you see if you can find some firewood around town?"

They set forth merrily and Janie was back in a few minutes with some excelsior. The older children were gone for a couple of hours. But then I heard a lot of noise in the yard and looked out to see Larry and Lynn, with a dozen or so helpers, happily breaking up old planks so they would fit the fireplace.

"We got you some wood," Larry said, when I walked out to the yard.

"Where'd you find it?" I asked.

"Oh, up the road. We can get all you want."

"Well, bring us a big pile and I'll buy you all a treat."

For the rest of that Saturday afternoon, Larry and his seventeen dwarfs hauled planks and half-rotten two-by-fours until it looked as if I had wood enough to last out a winter in the Yukon.

"Where are you getting all this?" I asked finally. "I hunted all over town and darned if I could find any wood."

"You just don't know where to look," Larry replied.

We kept warm that night. The fire was roaring by now and I got up several times during the night to put more wood on the blaze. The next day, it was just as cold as it had been out-

[114]

side, but the fat pine kept the house almost comfortable. We spent most of that Sunday near the hearth, making Valentines.

The sun came out the following morning and the house slowly began to warm up. By lunch time, I had let the fire die out and, seeing that the weather had returned to normal, I started to the store. There I found Buttons in high good humor. He was unusually cordial to me.

"If you come back here next winter, you can live in one of my cabins," he said happily.

"Going to start work on them?" I asked. "What about the old man's chicken house?"

He looked a little puzzled, then grinned at me knowingly.

"It got tore down over the week end," he said.

"Somebody tore it down?"

Again Buttons gave me the puzzled look. "I don't rightly know," he grinned, "but I heard some children tore it down and sold it for firewood. The old man's out looking for them now."

Suddenly, I let out a groan. "He's trying to find out who did it?" I asked anxiously.

"Yes, suh. Says he's going to set the sheriff on them."

I left the store abruptly and ran all the way home. I looked anxiously about to see whether I could spot Old Man Holmes, the sheriff, or both. But the coast was clear. By the time I reached the house, I was sweating profusely in the bright sun. Shucking off my sweater, I began to move the rest of the woodpile into my living room. But soon I realized that I had succeeded in concealing nothing. Because of the condition of my blinds, the wood was clearly visible to anyone passing, by. My only thought now was to destroy the evidence, and

[115]

the only place available for such a purpose was the fireplace. So I kindled a blaze and began to stoke the fire.

By now, the mercury outside had climbed into the high seventies, and I could see tourists taking sun baths on the beach. But I shucked my shirt and threw more wood on the fire. In the living room, the mercury had long since passed ninety and was now in the general area where a blast furnace is maintained. I piled some more wood on the fire and went outside for a breath of cool air. Just then, a neighbor passed and, noting the column of smoke coming out of my chimney, asked:

"You still cold in there?"

"Just a little," I replied, wiping the sweat off my face quickly.

After that, I decided to stay in the house. So, all during the afternoon, I remained in the room burning wood—with the Florida sun beating down on the roof in a fashion to make the Chamber of Commerce extremely proud. I stripped down at last to a pair of shorts and dashed to the shower every ten or fifteen minutes to cool off my fevered skin. My temper was going up with the temperature and I was waiting, with grim determination, for the hour when my son and heir would come home from school. Just a few minutes before he was due to arrive, I had managed to burn all the wood—except for one small plank. Now I sat down, with this in my lap, to wait for him.

He burst into the house in his normal fashion but ground to a sudden stop when he saw me.

"Wow!" he said, "it's hot in here. What's the fire going for?"

"Come here, Junior," I said, in no uncertain tone.

"What's the matter?" he asked.

"Bend over."

[116]

"What'd I do?"

Before answering that question, I made a sound connection between the paddle and his back side.

"This," I said, winding up for another swat, "will teach you to go around tearing down people's chicken houses without asking them."

Wham! went the paddle again.

"Wait a minute, Pop," he said, straightening up. "He said we could have it."

I paused in mid-air.

"Old Man Holmes said you could have his chicken house?" I demanded incredulously.

"No. That wasn't his chicken house we brought home. That was Luther's old cow shed. He said we could tear it down."

"Well, then who stole Old Man Holmes's chicken house?"

"Oh, that was some gang of kids from over by the tracks. The sheriff's picked them up hours ago."

Chapter Eleven

THE presence of a man who kept house for three young children—getting them off to school every day, feeding them, and keeping them in clean clothes—was enough to challenge the curiosity of the people of our village. The fact that it was not possible for me to pull down the shades in our house made our life almost completely open to view. In the early morning, I could be seen in the kitchen in my pajamas, squeezing out oranges and frying eggs for breakfast. Everyone knew when I burned the toast and whether I made the beds before noon. When my typewriter could be heard for any length of time, it informed the village that I was having stew for dinner, had left the house unswept, or was taking some other housekeeping short cut to find time to write. My children were cross-examined by the townspeople for details of our life and, from time to time, other children who came to the house showed such a lively interest in some particular phase of our existence that I could only conclude that they were trying to clear up some mystery existing in a dark corner which was not clearly visible from the street. The mothers of the town regarded my operation with suspicion—sometimes deep and sometimes amused—and they were never quite sure whether it was safe to permit their offspring to spend much time around our house.

I really tried to make our home as normal as possible, so that my children could have friends around and would feel that they were living like People. But it was difficult for me to maintain the appearance of normality, in the eyes of the local citizens, because things were always happening. There was the time, for instance, when a couple of friends from Orlando came to see us. Most people had friends who came to see them, but my friends had to arrive in an airplane. It was a small sea-plane and they landed it on the lake in front of the house. This sort of thing did not happen every year, and by the time the plane had taxied up to the beach near our place, the school had been given a recess, the store had shut down, and dozens of people had gathered in our front yard. My friends stayed for a time and, as they were getting ready to depart, they suggested that Larry might like to take a short hop.

"Boy!" he said, bug-eyed.

Then Larry spotted his closest pal in the crowd and asked eagerly:

"Can he come too?"

My friends said they had no objection, and so the boys climbed into the plane. It had just taken off when I heard a woman's voice demand excitedly:

"Where's Melvin? Where's Melvin?"

I turned around to see the mother of Larry's schoolmate approaching me, her eyes wide with alarm.

"Somebody said he's up in that airplane," she said, almost hysterically. "Where's my little boy?"

I tried to shrink a few sizes, so as to make less of a target.

Then I pointed to the plane which was circling over the lake.

"He went up with Larry," I said meekly. "Just for a short hop."

"Ohhhhh!" she said, with real anguish.

The plane disappeared from sight and the mother was beginning to sway gently, as if she were going to topple over. The whole thing had happened so quickly that I hadn't taken the time to worry, but now I was beginning to pace nervously. For the next ten minutes there was no sign of the plane, and I listened anxiously for anything that might sound like a loud crash. At last, the plane came back in view and began to circle the lake at a fairly high altitude.

"There," I told the mother, "they're back all right."

"Oh, how could you let him go without asking me?" she said angrily. "How could you do such a thing?"

"They're all right," I said stoutly. "I'm not worried . . ."

Just then, the plane went into a spin. I could feel every hair on my head stand up, turn gray, and collapse. I heard a moan and reached over just in time to catch the fainting woman. I didn't even look at her as I held her up, but kept watching with horror as the plane fell slowly, silently. Suddenly, when it was three or four hundred feet above the water, the motor roared and it pulled out of the spin. I lay the mother gently down on the ground and found a tree to serve as a prop for *me*. No one in the crowd was paying the slightest attention to us. I didn't look up again until I heard the plane stop on the shore. Then I saw that Melvin's mother had waded out to meet it. I got up and walked weakly to the beach.

The two boys jumped out, a little dazed but looking very happy. Melvin's mother started reading the riot act to him.

[120]

"What happened?" I demanded when my friend, the aviator, reached shore. "I thought you were all dead ducks."

He was bewildered by my excited tone.

"Oh, that spin—" he said easily. "The boys wanted to do a stunt, so I put the plane in a spin for them."

"I thought my stomach was coming out," said Melvin.

His mother was glowering at us and, I think, taking a deep breath to really tell us off.

"It was Melvin's idea," said Larry, just in the nick of time. "He thought that just plain flying was dull."

Melvin got a sudden yank and his mother marched him off. After that, I didn't think that any child in town would be allowed within a hundred yards of my house, but somehow it didn't work out that way. Half of the children set up shop on my front steps, in hopes that the plane would come back another day and take them for a ride. But at least a dozen mothers warned me that if I ever let their children go flying, they'd see that I was horsewhipped. To lend further luster to our reputation for oddness, on Lincoln's Birthday Larry decided to read the Gettysburg address at school, and there were some who suggested that exposing southern children to such propaganda was probably subversive.

When Larry reminded me, one day in March, that his birthday was coming along soon, I suggested that we simply have a quiet family celebration.

"What!" he said, outraged. "Why I've already invited all the kids at school."

"I told uh nursery school kids to come too," Janie said helpfully.

"No you don't," said Larry heatedly. "I won't have those little brats . . ."

"Well at least, Larry," said Janie solemnly, "'Ey don't say 'gotdan' and swear like Melvin."

"Now wait a minute, you two," I said. "Don't I have anything to say about this?"

"It's *my* birthday," said Larry.

"Yes," said Janie.

The logic of this statement rather overwhelmed me. So, in my anxiety to let the children establish the usual sort of relations with their friends, I told Larry he could have the kind of party he wanted. It developed that what he had in mind was something just slightly more elaborate than a New Orleans Mardi Gras. For days, we talked of nothing else. I grew more and more apprehensive as the birthday approached. I had grown somewhat accustomed to having scores of children roaming around the place, but my knees began to weaken at the thought of having every kid in town in the house at one time—with nobody but me to stand between them and the realization of their instincts for destruction. I knew that if anything went wrong, it would substantiate the belief of the normal people that their children should stay away from our place. All of this gave me that same feeling of loneliness and incompetence which had nearly paralyzed me on Christmas Eve.

On the day of the great event, I scrubbed the house thoroughly. This was not because I expected the children to notice whether it was clean, but because I thought that some of the parents might want to look over the place to make sure it was fit for their progeny. I was beaten down from scrubbing, dusting, and mopping by the time I got around to making the cakes. Larry had given me some very specific orders in connection with the celebration. For one thing, he informed me that every year he had a birthday cake of a different color. This was his year to have a cake with blue icing—not navy blue, but a sort of turquoise. He must have home-made vanilla ice cream, and would I mind coloring that blue, too? I made two cakes of turquoise blue and a gallon of vanilla ice cream, same shade, and, half an hour before party time, I was ready for a shower. In the process I had pretty well covered myself with blue food coloring and of course, it was while I was in this condition that one of the mothers knocked at the door to ask what time the party was to start.

Just as I started my shower, I heard another knock at the front door and found two young guests arriving half an hour early. Their faces were shining, their clothes were clean, and each carried a neatly wrapped present. Suggesting that they wait in the yard until the other children arrived, I went back to my shower. I managed to turn myself white again, and just in time. For the two early arrivals now reappeared, accompanied by more children than I had ever seen in one place before. I was sure that the Pied Piper had passed that way and left his retinue.

Within a few minutes, I had children on the furniture, under the furniture, in the closets, swinging from the ceiling, sitting on the mantle, and hanging out of the windows. They were playing cops and robbers, cowboys and Indians, mommas and poppas, and hide and seek, all at once. After a brief skirmish, I got things under control and started the games which Larry had planned for the party. They played pin the tail on the donkey, musical chairs, and drop the handkerchief until the last vestige of pleasure had been wrung out of these games. Then I decided it must be time for refreshments.

I lighted the candles on the cake, set out the ice cream and punch, and started serving. Everyone was delighted with the blue motif—which was now one hundred per cent, because Larry had added some blue coloring to the punch—and there was a brief, but wonderful, moment of silence when everyone got a mouthful at the same time. But it wasn't long before everyone was finished. A couple of the boys filled their water pistols in the punch bowl and started to spray the company. Someone else decided to defend himself with a hunk of cake fired from a slingshot. At this moment, I rushed in with second helpings and put down the incipient riot.

But the seconds were soon exhausted and someone got the idea of dipping the little girls' pigtails in the punch. I rushed in with third helpings, but the children were too full to eat and so they merely used this extra serving as ammunition. Within a few minutes, my living room looked as if a blue blizzard were taking place. Cake, ice cream, and streams of punch were flying in all directions. I rushed in to restore order, but was stopped short by a blob of blue ice cream aimed at my face with deadly accuracy. Then I grabbed Larry and started talking:

"Here's some chalk," I said. "You start out and make a trail for these kids to follow. Chalk up some messages and arrows on the walls. I don't care how far it goes—just so it's far away. I'll turn the kids out in about five minutes, and the first one who finds the end of the trail can have this penknife."

"Okay," he said, and set off.

I went into the living room and restored order. I promised the kids I would do some card tricks, and while I was shuffling the cards, I looked around. The room was splattered with blue from one end to the other, but no more thoroughly than were the little guests. Some children were blue from ear to ear, and some were blue from head to toes. There were beautiful white dresses, streaked with blue, and clean white shirts, soaked with blue. There were little girls whose pigtails had been dunked in blue and little boys who had sat in blue. And then there was me—covered with blue, up, down, and around.

After five minutes, I turned the pack loose and collapsed into a chair—not even noticing, for a full three minutes, that I was sitting in a dish of ice cream. When I did feel the cold trickling through, it didn't seem to matter. All I cared about was the knowledge that the howling mob had gone off to howl somewhere else. It was at least half an hour before Larry got back.

"Boy, Pop, I made a real trail," he announced breathlessly. "That'll take care of them for the rest of the day."

"You don't happen to have that knife on you, do you?" I asked.

"No. I hid it at the end of the trail. Why?"

"Oh, I just thought I might cut my throat, that's all."

When a little strength returned, I sat about to repair the damage in what we now called The Blue Room. It took me well over an hour and a half, and just as I was finished, Larry came home to announce that the first contestant had crossed the line and had found the prize. After a while, a group of children came by to see what, if anything, was doing. I knew they had been to the party because they were all blue. They were a little crestfallen to find that the hostilities had ended and wandered on home sadly. When their mothers saw the delicate tints with which they were decorated, I knew that my name was going to be mud. Taking a kid up in an airplane was one thing, but dyeing every child in town turquoise was something else again.

[125]

I started to fix supper but was slowed down considerably by a steady stream of visitors. They were of two classes: children still returning from the treasure hunt and parents looking for children who had not yet returned. The parents made me very nervous, because I was expecting at any moment to be set upon by those who had to do the washing for my indigo guests.

Larry was very happy about the whole afternoon. The party had exceeded his wildest expectations and had undoubtedly been the social event of the local season.

"Next year," he enthused, "I want a red, white, and blue cake and ice cream."

"You'll have to see somebody else about that, Bub," I said. "Personally, I'm out of the birthday-party business. Especially technicolor birthdays."

Just then, someone else knocked at the door. It was another mother.

"Is Lee here?" she asked.

"I don't think so," I said wearily. "Everyone went on a treasure hunt and some of them haven't come back yet."

She looked dubious, as if she suspected that I had cut up her Lee for chops.

"His sister said he didn't go on the treasure hunt," she insisted. "She just got home. When I washed the mud off her, I found all that blue stuff. But Lee didn't come home for supper."

I called Larry and Lynn and they couldn't remember what had happened to Lee. Just then, Janie appeared.

" 'Ere's some kid in uh bedroom," she said, "readin' funnies."

We looked, and there was Lee, all right, half buried in a stack of comic books which had been among the day's offerings to the birthday child. His hair was covered with a thin coat of blue cake icing. His mother gasped and dragged him away.

"Just out of curiosity," she said as they reached the door, "what were you doing? Letting them pretend they were Easter eggs?"

I offered an explanation, but the whole thing sounded so ridiculous when I got into the blue icing, blue vanilla ice cream, and blue punch, that I gave it up. We went back to the supper table and had taken a few bites when there was another knock at the door. This time it was a father.

"I was looking for my boy, Jimmy," he said. "He's supposed to be at this party where everybody got colored blue."

"I think all the children have gone," I said. "They went on a treasure hunt."

"Oh," he said, and went away.

We were eating dessert when there came another knock.

"I'm Jimmy's mother," the caller announced. She seemed irate, but I couldn't make out whether Jimmy had, or had not, come home.

"Yes?" I said. "Won't you come in?"

"Are you sure he isn't here?"

"Well," I said dubiously, "we did find one in the bedroom a little while ago. Want to help us look around? You might recognize him easier."

We turned the place upside down, from garage to attic and from closet to refrigerator.

"I tell you," Larry said, "I remember seeing him leave on the treasure hunt and I'm sure he hasn't been back since."

By the look she gave me, I could tell that her worst fears were confirmed. She went away, shaking her head sadly, and I knew she was reproaching herself for being so foolhardy as to allow her child to come into my house. We finished supper, washed the dishes, and I chased the children off to bed. I was as tired as an old dishrag myself, and when I saw that it was nine o'clock, I decided to hit the hay. Two minutes later, I was sound asleep. And three minutes after that, I was awakened by the sound of a persistent knock on the door. I got up and opened the door, but in the dark I could see no one. Then I heard a small voice and looked down to see the dim figure of a little boy.

"Larry home?" he asked.

"He's in bed. Asleep," I replied menacingly.

"Oh," he said, but didn't move.

"I wonder, could you tell me, Mr. Toombs, did anyone find the prize in that treasure hunt you all were having?"

"Sure. Sure. Hours ago."

"Well, I just got to the end of the trail, but they weren't nothing there."

"It was a penknife, for a prize," I said wearily. "I don't remember who it was found it. But it was all over long before dark. Hours ago."

"Yes, suh," said the small voice.

"Well, you better get on home now."

"Yes, suh. I hope they saved my dinner."

I had a sudden, sinking feeling.

"Hey," I called to the retreating figure, "what's your name?"

"Jimmy," he said sadly.

Chapter Twelve

THIS was not going to be a good morning. I could see that.

First, the dog who, after three months of almost daily punishments, was still not entirely housebroken, had given me a reminder of how stupid he could be. In my anger, I had spanked him and put him outside—the latter maneuver being always a sad mistake because, among other things, he had not yet learned to come when called. Nor would he even stand still and allow himself to be caught. Whenever he managed to get out of the yard, as he had this morning, it meant a merry chase through the village. Larry and I had pursued him this morning through briar patches, under houses, through ditches, and under automobiles. Finally someone in town, tiring of listening to our calls of "Here Tonker" caught him for us as usual. This put me in a bad enough humor, but it was only the beginning.

I had been boiling out a soupbone and had set a big kettle of the stock on one side of the stove to cool. Janie decided that the Tweenies needed to have their dresses washed and had mistaken the soup stock for soapy water. This did not improve the soup, the doll clothes, nor my disposition. Then I found Lynn wandering around with that vacant look indicating that she had lost something else. After questioning her closely, I found that the day before she had decided to go wading. She had taken off her new shoes along the beach and couldn't remember now exactly where that had happened.

"Maybe a dog ran off with them," she suggested.

Since it was Saturday, it was housecleaning day and I never let the children go out until they had picked up their room and helped me make the beds. We were all confined indoors and were being subjected to the latest manifestation of the fact that Larry was a growing boy. He had now abandoned the Confederacy, his study of the *Public Papers of Franklin Roosevelt*, and his fleet of sponge-diving boats and was absorbed by a new interest—popular music.

He had begun in a modest way, listening each week to a radio program called the *Hit Parade*. Soon, he became obsessed with it and bought a notebook in which he would list the ten tunes which were played on the program and the order of their popularity. Then he began to write down the words to the songs, and then to sing them—incessantly. He was quite tone deaf, so that every song had the same tune but different words. In order to learn all these songs, of course, he had to listen to popular music on the radio all the time, and anyone in the family who made any noise while he was listening was soundly berated.

Now he had discovered a new program on a local station which lasted for an hour on Saturday mornings. It was called the *Hill Billy Hit Parade*, and it featured one of those rural quartets —four sets of enlarged adenoids and a guitar—which droned the dreary laments most favored currently by devotees of folk music. The program was on at the moment and I was suffering acutely.

[130]

I heard the sound of an automobile horn which I recognized as John's.

"My cup overfloweth," I muttered as I walked to the door to admit him.

"Aren't you ready yet?" he demanded.

"Ready for what?" I replied testily.

"To go to Gainesville. Didn't you get my letter?"

"No, I did *not* get your letter."

A look of disbelief crossed his face and then he reached into his jacket pocket, fumbled around for a minute, and apparently found what he had been afraid he was going to find.

"I'll be darned," he said wonderingly. "I forgot to mail it."

He laughed uproariously and this started him coughing. In between gasps, he told me that he had decided that the Toombs ought to have a little change. So he had suggested to one of his friends, whom we had met, that we pay them a week-end visit in Gainesville.

"He's supposed to pick us up at my house in an hour," said John, getting frantic again. "So hurry up."

I entered a number of objections, but John won the debate when he pointed out that the people in Gainesville had a genuine bathtub with hot and cold running water. We had spent that winter trying to keep clean in a cold shower, or a washtub full of hot water, and a real tub sounded like something in a fairy tale. Within fifteen minutes, I had the whole mob dressed, packed, and ready to move—and had forgotten my troubles.

"How's about having some lunch before we go?" I asked John.

"Haven't got time," he replied. "He'll probably be waiting at my house for us when we get there. We'll pick up something, somewhere."

When we reached John's house, there was no sign of our

friend so we settled down to wait. After an hour had passed, I suggested to John that we go out for lunch.

"He's likely to be here any minute now," said John, "and I'm afraid to leave. Let's just get a snack out of the icebox."

He produced some cold cuts and potato salad and set places for us.

"Aren't you eating?" I asked.

"Think I'll just have a beer and some eggs," he replied.

When our host still had not appeared by the time we had finished eating, John decided to go to a neighbor's house and telephone Gainesville. He was back a few minutes later, grinning sheepishly.

"It was last week end that we were supposed to go up there," he said. "Guess I got mixed up."

"So?" I said. "What are we going to do now?"

"Oh, we'll go anyway. He's sending a car down to pick us up. It's just an hour's drive."

"Why don't we use your car?" I asked.

"Something's wrong with the radiator," he explained. "I'm afraid to drive that far."

We finally reached Gainesville, in time for dinner. I put the youngest one to bed and the older children went to a movie. As the evening wore on, I became aware of an uneasy feeling in my stomach. It wasn't long after Larry and Lynn had gone to bed that I made my excuses and started for my room. I stopped to see if the little girls were tucked in snugly and found Lynn sitting up in bed.

"I feel funny, Daddy," she said.

"Me, too," said Janie from deep down in the covers.

"So do I," I confessed. "Maybe we ate something that upset us."

Just then, John appeared in the door and said excitedly:

"Hey, hurry upstairs. Larry's sick at his stomach."

I raced up to the bedroom where the boy had been sleeping and had just reached his bed when our hostess called up the stairs:

"Someone had better come down here. These little girls are sick to their stomachs."

John took a quick look at me.

"What's the matter?" he asked.

"Where's the nearest bathroom?" I said wildly. "I'm sick, too."

Ptomaine had caught up with us at last and the rest of that night was an agony. The children and I were something less than perfect guests that week end. John, who had not been affected, worried so much that he almost brought his stomach ulcer back to life. When we had recovered sufficiently to discuss the matter, I tried to trace the poison back to its source, feeling that my reputation as a housekeeper had been besmirched. The only thing that all four of us had all eaten the day before, it developed, was the potato salad we had for lunch at John's.

"How long had that stuff been in your icebox?" I asked him.

"Oh, I don't know," he said. "Just a week or two, I guess."

"Say no more," I replied.

We went home that afternoon and, as I left the car, I said to John:

"Well, it was a *change*—"

He looked at me without understanding.

"First time we've had ptomaine," I said.

The whole thing made John feel very bad and he did his best to make it up to us. He began to keep dates and even arrived more or less on time. We made another week-end trip to Gainesville—eating lunch at our house before leaving this time—without mishap. Lulled into a false sense of security by the sudden evidence of responsibility and promptness which John was now showing, I began to depend upon him again for little favors. When, in the middle of May, we had decided to head north, John insisted that he be allowed to drive us to the train.

"Swell," I said. "The train leaves at 2:00 P.M. You'd better come for us about 11:30."

It was normally only half an hour's drive to the station, but I intended to give John—even the new, reformed John—plenty of leeway. The night before we were to leave, I had a last roundup for Tonker and, having caught him, put him in his crate and sent him to the station along with the rest of our baggage. It took a truck to haul it all—with the dog, two cats, four trunks, and fifteen assorted containers full of toys. I carried my precious manuscripts and I allowed Janie to keep out only five of her dolls named Tweenie.

"But Daddy," she said tearfully, as I put the surplus dolls in a trunk. "'Ey'll be lonely. And so will I."

The morning we were to leave, I cleaned out the house and tried to leave in good order those few pieces of furniture which had survived the cold spell. We were ready to leave by 11:30, but we didn't really expect John to be on time. I wasn't even worried when he failed to appear before 12:00. But when 12:30 arrived and John didn't, I grew apprehensive. By one o'clock, I was frantic. At 1:15, I began to hunt around the neighborhood for someone who could drive us to town and by 1:30 had succeeded in locating a friend, with automobile. But just then John appeared. Great geysers of steam were pouring out of his car.

"Quick," he gasped. "Get some water for the radiator."

"What happened to you?" I demanded.

[134]

"I overslept. Then this radiator went bad on me again. I had to stop for water five times on the way down."

"We've got another ride," I told him. "The train leaves in twenty-five minutes!"

"I'll get you there," John said, beginning to puff as hard as his car.

"No thanks," I said hurriedly, "we're all set. Thanks."

But John was already transferring our baggage into his car and yelling at me to pour water in the radiator. There was only twenty minutes until train time as we set off in a cloud of dust. The children were having more fun than they'd had since the blue birthday party, but I was a nervous wreck. We had covered about two miles when a geyser of steam spouted out of the radiator. John. who had been traveling at top speed, slowed down to a crawl.

"We'll have to stop for more water," he said.

There was a service station about two miles ahead and we limped into that. Within a few seconds, the cloud of steam around the car had settled sufficiently so that the attendant could find us. I jumped out and ran toward the road.

"Hey, where're you going?" John called.

"While you're getting water," I yelled back, "I'll try to hitch a ride."

Unfortunately, the car was filled before any traffic passed, so it was necessary to take off with John again. We had reached the half-way point—with seven minutes left until train time—when Old Faithful erupted once more. John wheeled into another service station. I saw a grimy attendant leaning against a battered Ford and I leaped out of John's car and ran toward him.

[135]

"For five bucks," I yelled, "can you get us to town in five minutes?"

"I'll try," he said.

I yanked the kids out of John's car and we grabbed as much baggage as we could at first try. I yelled to John to ship the left-over things to us in Maryland and we set off with our new chauffeur. For once, nobody in my family said a word for a full five minutes. As we reached the outskirts of town, my heart sank. I could see by the courthouse clock that it was exactly two o'clock.

"Well," I said, breaking the silence, "I guess we missed it."

"Missed what?" asked the driver.

"The two o'clock train," I said miserably.

"Shucks," he said, slowing down immediately. "You all should of told me. They changed the schedule yesterday. Train don't come in until three o'clock now."

I heaved a mighty sigh of relief.

"It's a good thing, too," said Lynn. "Now we'll have time to go back and get our things out of John's car."

"Oh, he'll ship them to us," I said casually.

"Daddy?" said Lynn hesitantly.

"Yes?"

"Aren't the train tickets in your raincoat pocket?"

"Yes," I said. Then in a sudden surge of panic I turned toward her and roared, "that raincoat was the only blessed thing I gave you to carry. Did you forget it?"

"But Daddy," she sobbed, "Janie was having so much trouble picking up all her dolls in John's car that I had to help her. Then you started yelling to hurry up, so I forgot and left your coat in the car."

"Okay. Okay. Stop your bawling. We'll have to go back and get the coat."

[136]

Our driver shot me a weary look.

"Back to the service station?" he asked.

"I guess so. Then will you bring us in again?"

He nodded sullenly.

For the next few miles, no one spoke. In silence, we started up a hill, about a mile from the service station. Suddenly, the car started to knock.

"Bearing's burned out," said the driver, pulling over to the side of the road.

"Can't you just get up the hill?" I said. "We could coast from there."

He shot me a dark look and shook his head angrily.

We piled out and for a moment stood looking at each other in bewilderment. Just then, I heard the loud blast of a familiar horn and looked up to see John's car sailing serenely down the hill. He stopped and yelled:

"What happened?"

I gave him a brief run-down of our troubles.

"Hop in," he said cheerfully.

Since there was no way out, I began transferring baggage and children to his car again and paid off the garage man. Then John, over my somewhat selfish protests, insisted on pushing the man's car to the top of the hill, so he could coast home.

"You better not put too much strain on this thing," I said anxiously.

"It's running like a clock," he announced happily, as we heaved the other car up the hill.

By the time we had sent the garage man on his way, most of the hour of grace I had earned was exhausted. I was beginning to get nervous again.

"Are you sure you can make it to the station?" I asked John.

"I told you I'd get you there," he said airily. "You worry too much."

"Or not enough," I said.

We had reached the bottom of that hill now and were starting up another when John's car erupted again. In the distance I thought I could hear the whistle of the three o'clock train approaching town.

"Hold your hats, kids," I said, as John looked about wildly for another service station, "here we go again."

Chapter Thirteen

IN spite of John, we caught the train and with Larry, Lynn, Janie, and five of the dolls named Tweenie, I arrived in Washington early the next morning. The two cats and Tonker were on a different train, which was due to come in four hours later. With my caravan, I started for my family's home, where my father was waiting to drive us to the country that afternoon.

"Can we get our bikes now?" asked Larry.

"Could you wait until we eat breakfast?" I asked.

"I guess so," he said unhappily.

By the time I had finished half a cup of coffee, Larry was dressed and ready to go to the bicycle store. He was annoyed because I had refused to buy the bikes while we were still in Florida and he wanted no further delay. Choosing a bicycle for Lynn was no problem, but Larry had to shop around until he found one equipped with everything except jet propulsion and a Norden bombsight. We were back at the house before noon and I called the baggage office at the station to see whether the animals had arrived on schedule.

When I described the shipment to the clerk, there was a moment of silence.

"I think you'd better come down here," he said hesitantly. "There's been a little mix-up about that shipment."

I slammed the receiver and rushed down town in my father's car. Of course, I told myself, there would have to be some mix-up—that worthless dog couldn't possibly travel from one place to another without causing trouble. Poor Larry had forgotten all about his shiny new bicycle and was sitting beside me fretting like a new father. When we got to the baggage office, I found a clerk on duty and identified myself. He gestured toward a crate which I recognized as Tonker's.

"One of the men thought he was thirsty," the clerk said. "So he opened the crate to give him some water. And he broke out."

"My gosh," I said. "Where did he go? Did someone catch him?"

"That's a mighty hard dog to catch," the clerk said. This seemed a remarkable bit of understatement.

Just then the phone rang and I heard the clerk say:

"On the Capitol steps? Well, the owner's right here. I'll send him over. Glad you found him."

Then he turned to me and explained:

"I've got my whole force out chasing that dog. There's not a bit of baggage moving around here. One of the men just called in and said someone had seen a hound dog on the Capitol steps. You go on over there and maybe they'll have him by the time you arrive."

Larry and I ran the three blocks to the Capitol and there found two uniformed baggage smashers from the station, perspiring freely and looking confused.

"Someone told us he went in the Capitol," one of them said.

[141]

I led the search party into the Capitol itself and, finally, located a breathless Capitol policeman who'd just been chasing a little hound dog. The dog, he explained, had somehow got on the floor of the Senate which, luckily, was not in session at that hour. The dog had mistaken one of the desks on the Republican side for a fireplug.

"He's a mighty shy dog," said the policeman, "I couldn't catch him."

"Which way did he go?" I asked.

"Downstairs," the policeman said. "I lost him when he ran into the subway tunnel."

Like four characters in a Keystone Kop comedy, we rushed downstairs and found the entrance to the miniature subway which runs from the Capitol to the Senate Office Building. We found a sign which said "For Senators Only," but there was no car at the platform.

"Here, Tonker! Here, Tonker," Larry began to yell and the call echoed down the tunnel.

A few minutes later, a car pulled in and a distinguished-looking man stepped off. Larry was still yelling frantically for the dog and I was whistling as loud as I could. The baggage men were just standing there, probably trying to decide whether there wasn't some easier way they could earn a living.

"Looking for a dog?" the distinguished-looking man asked.

"Yeah," said Larry. "Did you see him? A little brown and black and white dog?"

"Yes. I tried to pet him and he snapped at me. Then he ran out of the Senate Office Building."

"I'm sorry about that," I said hastily. "He's been raised in the South. I guess you're the first Republican he ever saw, Senator Vandenberg."

We started off at a dead gallop again, but by the time we got to the Senate Office Building, all we could find were two guards who swore that he had gone in opposite directions.

"I guess we'd better get back to work," said the baggage men.

Larry and I started down the street, whistling and calling —although I don't know why, for Tonker never came when he was called. We attracted a great deal of attention, and every few minutes someone would stop to assure us that they had seen the dog, just around the corner. All afternoon, until we were hoarse and exhausted, we roamed the streets and alleys of the teeming city, looking for that dog. Everyone we asked was sure that he had just passed that way—but their candidate always turned out to be a chow, a police dog, or a pony.

The baggage office at the station had at last got back to the business of moving baggage, so we picked up the cats, our trunks and boxes and went sadly home. While Tonker could not qualify as one of my favorite characters, I was depressed by the thought of such a simple-minded little country dog wandering the streets of a big city. He had hardly ever seen a motor vehicle, and I died a thousand deaths as I thought of him running in front of streetcars and coal trucks—for the loss of the other dog, Tinker, was still fresh in my mind.

When I got to my family's home, I called the police, the dog pound, and the "Lost Ad" department of the newspapers. All thought of leaving for the country had been put out of mind, and now we settled down to wait for Tonker to come back, dead or alive. I called a few of the reporters I had once worked with on the local newspapers and related my tale of woe. It was such a silly story—a man trying to move forty pieces of baggage, three small children, two cats, and a hound dog from Florida to Washington and then losing the dog—that it struck the fancy of the newspaper writers. So the next morning, the papers devoted half or three quarters of a column to the stirring saga of Tonker, the country hound dog who had got lost in the big city.

As I sat down to breakfast, the phone began to ring. There were people in all parts of town who had seen big dogs, little dogs, white dogs, and black cats wandering around their neighborhood and who wondered whether I had found Tonker. It was about eleven o'clock, and I was worn out with all the unhelpful helpful suggestions, when a man called in from the suburbs.

"I was passing the Washington Monument this morning," he said. "And I saw a little beagle hound curled up on the grass asleep in the rain."

"You're sure it was a beagle?" I asked, having learned by now that people were likely to mistake anything with more than two legs for a beagle.

"Oh yes, I used to raise them," he said.

I thanked him and called Larry. This was our first definite identification of a beagle, so I told the boy:

"Here's some cab fare. Chase on down to the Monument grounds and see if that really is Tonker. I'll stay here by the phone and you call me back in half an hour."

Larry took off like a rocket and, about fifteen minutes later, the phone rang again.

"This is the Internal Revenue Bureau," a girl's voice said. "I mean, I work here."

"Yes?" I said.

"Did you lose a little dog?"

"To say the least," I replied wearily.

"A little brown and black and white dog with big ears?"

[144]

"Yes," I said, getting excited now.

"Well, I just saw him run through our parking lot. They're trying to catch him, but he's too shy."

The Internal Revenue building is just a short distance from the Monument grounds, and I began to have hopes that Tonker, even though he didn't have sense enough to come in out of the rain, might somehow have survived a night on the city's streets.

"My son is down near there," I said to the girl. "He's a blond boy and he's wearing a red shirt. I'll send him down to your building as soon as he calls me up and you show him where the dog is, will you?"

The next call came from one of my newspaper friends at police headquarters.

"There's a complaint about a stray dog digging up the lawn at the Department of Justice," he said. "Could that be your mutt?"

"Get the FBI on the case," I yelled. "Get some cops down there, too, will you?"

"I'll get them to run a squad car down," my friend said. "But I don't really think it's an FBI case."

"He's an interstate dog," I insisted hopefully. "See what you can do."

Just then, Larry called in and I sent him hot-footing down Constitution Avenue to the Internal Revenue and Justice Department buildings. Then, I sat back and held my breath, waiting for Larry, government girls, squad cars, and/or the FBI to close in on Tonker. A few minutes later, the girl from Internal Revenue phoned again.

"I found your son," she said happily. "But now the dog's gone."

"Thanks," I said. "Ask him to go on down toward the Justice Department. There's a report of a stray dog there."

[145]

My friend, the police reporter, called next to report that a complaint had just come in from the Smithsonian Institution that a dog was loose in their museum.

"I don't know what the rumpus was all about at the Smithsonian, but they were pretty excited," he said. "That's just across the street from the Justice Department, you know."

By now, I felt like Eisenhower on D-Day. With all my forces deployed, I had only to wait and see what would happen. Tonker didn't have a chance, now, I was sure. Ten minutes later, the girl from Internal Revenue called again. I could hear the scream of sirens as she talked.

"Where's the little boy?" she asked excitedly.

"Isn't he down there?" I asked.

"I lost him in the crowd," she said.

"The crowd?"

"Yes," she said happily, "you should see the excitement. Traffic's all tied up and there must be half a dozen big fat policemen chasing that little dog around Constitution Avenue. But he's got a bone in his mouth and won't let them get near him. I think the dog would come to the little boy."

I had a frantic feeling. There was Tonker—just within arm's length, and now Larry was lost.

"Wait a minute," the girl said. "There's the little boy. He's running after the dog, too. I'll call you back."

There was a long interval, during which I had to sit and wonder whether just this once Tonker wouldn't come to Larry when he was called. Then the phone rang.

"He's got the dog," said the girl. "He wants to know what to do with him."

First, I tried to steady myself. Then I reminded myself not

[146]

to make any rude suggestions as to what the little boy could do with that dog. Finally, I managed to say:

"Tell him to get in a cab and come on home."

I thanked the young lady profusely and we hung up.

Pacing the floor, I felt like a man who had just won a four-engine airplane on a radio quiz show. Before long, the phone rang. It was the young lady again.

"The little boy's sitting on the curb at Eleventh and Constitution," she said. "They won't let him in a cab with the dog."

"I don't blame them," I said. "Tell him to sit there and I'll be down in a few minutes in the car."

It was raining a little when I pulled up at the downtown corner where Larry sat with his arms around Tonker. The crowd had all departed now and no one was paying any attention to the little tableau. Larry's hair was mussed and his clothes were muddy. Tonker was dirty and wet, but I noticed he was clinging still to that bone. I stopped the car across the street—right in front of the Smithsonian Museum—and waited for them to cross, since I couldn't make a turn.

Tonker jumped in the car without hesitation and I quickly rolled up my window to make sure he wouldn't escape. He was wagging his tail so hard that the car seemed to vibrate.

"He was *so* glad to see me, Daddy," said Larry happily. "Poor little fellow."

"Well," I said, turning around to look at the dog, "for once, I'm glad to see him. He isn't hurt, is he?"

"He's all right," said Larry. "But I wish he'd drop that bone."

"Take the filthy thing away from him," I told Larry.

"He won't let me. You know how fierce he is when he's got a bone."

[147]

I was just putting the car in gear to pull away when a uniformed guard came running out of the museum, waving frantically at me.

"Hey," he yelled. "Wait a minute."

He approached the car, stooped down to look at Tonker, and then rapped on the window. I rolled it down a little, but not so much that Tonker could get out.

"Is that the little dog that was running around in the museum a while ago?" he demanded angrily.

"I don't know," I said. "He's been running around everywhere. Maybe he was in there, too."

"Well, make him give me that bone. It's part of a rib off one of our dinosaur skeletons."

"Did he do *that?*" I asked, feigning an incredulity which I didn't entirely feel. My greatest surprise was that Tonker had not taken the whole dinosaur.

I reached back to get the bone away from Tonker.

"We don't allow no dogs in the museum," said the guard belligerently.

"Don't blame you a bit," I said, soothingly.

Tonker growled at me, as usual, when I put my hand out for the bone. This caused me to turn around and face him.

"Give me that bone, Tonker," I said, in a tone which, had he possessed any sense, would have caused him to run away again.

It did something to him, though, and for the first time in his life, Tonker obeyed me. I slipped the bone through the crack in the window to the guard and sped away.

"Isn't he cute?" Larry said, regarding his dog affectionately.

Chapter Fourteen

I HAVE seen houses hit by bombs that were in better shape than our cottage when we returned that spring. During the winter, my father had spent some week ends in the place. He had set up a wood stove and had experienced some difficulties in deciding on the best place to locate it. There were several holes in the ceiling where he had run up the stovepipe and then changed his mind. He had also found a sag in the living-room floor and had tried to jack up the house. As a result, where there had been a small valley, there was now a good-sized hill. The mice, who had been living in the place while we were away, were having a fine time doing belly-flops down the incline when we walked in. I was still shuddering at the thought of the work to make the place habitable when my father called to me from the yard. He was in high good spirits, now that spring and I had returned, and was full of more plans for construction than an Egyptian Pharaoh.

"Want to show you the garden," he said cheerfully.

During the winter, we had exchanged some correspondence on the subject of a vegetable garden. I had agreed that it might be a good idea to raise fresh produce for the table, and he had volunteered to get the ground ready. But I was hardly prepared for what he now showed me. He had hired a farmer to plow up about half the ground around the place and had then proceeded to plant almost every vegetable known to grow in the Western Hemisphere. Proudly, he led me down the rows, explaining what needed weeding, cultivating, and spraying.

"You'll have to take care of this," he said, "I'm going to be too busy with carpenter work this summer."

He couldn't have made me happier had he handed me a small family of young rattlesnakes to raise.

"If a man's time were worth anything," he said, thoughtfully, gazing at the expanse of garden, "I'm not sure this would be such a good idea."

All I did about the garden for the next ten days was to glance at it out of the window as I raced from one room of the house to another, trying to restore order. When I finally had time to work on the garden, I found that I was growing the world's handsomest collection of weeds. Getting rid of them took another week, and by then the house was a shambles again. It was obvious that I was trying to chew more than I could bite off and I began to cast about frantically for help. My eyes fell immediately upon three healthy children, who were eating three large meals a day and demanding no end of attention.

Since returning to Maryland, they had been very busy children. Lynn was trying to promote better relations between the two tomcats and the local song-birds and between Tonker, the rabbit hound, and the local bunnies. It kept her very busy, because by the time she had convinced a bird that it should not show hostility toward the cats, one of the cats would chase the bird. And by the time she had convinced a rabbit that Tonker's intentions were honorable, she would find that rabbit chasing Tonker through the briars.

Janie's family had increased somewhat since our return. She now had fifteen Tweenies and an Oriental doll—the only boy— named Foo Young. It was her habit to bring all of her family to the table for all meals and, until I broke up the practice, she had to give all sixteen children a taste of everything that she ate herself.

Larry had now fallen easily and naturally into the role of the junior Senator from Maryland. He had gone off on this tack as a result of reading a school book on governmental affairs. This had led him to read two more books, explaining in detail the workings of all the bureaus of the federal government. After that, he had studied the U.S. Constitution and written a critique of it. Now, he was having the *Congressional Record* sent to him and, even worse, was reading it. All of this study, naturally, consumed so much of his time that he had small opportunity to pick up his own clothes, wash dishes, or hoe the corn.

There were two reasons why I had failed to harness this child-power up to now. The first was that I had enough work to do, without getting the children to help me with it. And the second was that I didn't really know how to secure their cooperation. I was still convinced that there was a way it could be done, but my previous efforts at organizing systems to organize children had left me shaken and uncertain. It seemed to me that all of my systems had resulted in too much regimentation. I wanted to find some way to get the kids to behave like human beings, without making a full-time job of seeing that they did.

One night, I heard an experiment in child psychology dramatized on the radio. It described how a group of children had been organized into a club which had operated successively

[151]

under a benevolent dictatorship, a system of complete laissez faire and a democracy. The children had accomplished most and been happiest, the experiment showed, when given the freedom and responsibility of self-government. I pondered this lesson and finally called my youngsters together.

"I've got a new idea for us," I said.

Larry groaned loudly, because by now he had come to understand that most of my ideas had the concept of work as a basic tenet.

"Let's pretend this is the wilderness," I said, since that didn't require anyone to stretch his imagination too far, "and we are pioneers who have just moved here. Now we've got to set up a sort of government and all of us work to take our living off this place."

Everyone seemed to be quite intrigued so far.

"Are 'ere wild engines?" asked Janie, who had once seen a wild-west movie.

"No, I don't think so. But we'd better be ready in case there are."

Then I went on to describe the sort of society we would have to build—where we would all have certain responsibilities, certain freedoms, and certain benefits. We could achieve all this by agreeing upon certain rules of conduct and then working together to enforce the rules.

"In other words," I said, "we'll set up a sort of democratic government. We'll have an election and then we'll pass our own rules."

"I'll write a constitution," proposed the junior Senator eagerly.

"All right." I said. "Then we'll have a convention and talk it over."

While I battled weeds in the garden and litter in the house

for the next few days, the Senator was busy at his desk. At last, he called together the little band of hardy pioneers and read us his masterpiece:

Preamble: We, the United Toombs of America, in order to establish justice and insure liberty, do ordain and establish this Constitution.

Article 1: Any person whose last name is Toombs and who has attained the age of four shall be a citizen.

Article 2: The Legislative power shall be vested in a Congress that shall be composed of all the citizens. Laws shall be made by the Congress and penalties for violating same. The Congressmen shall receive a compensation.

Article 3: The Judicial Power shall be vested in a court which shall be composed of the citizens. Their duties shall be to try all persons accused of violating the laws. The members of the Court shall receive a compensation.

Article 5: Each citizen will be subject to penalties imposed by other members of the Court.

Article 6: No citizen shall be allowed to manhandle another citizen, i.e., kick, hit, slap, pull hair, push around or, especially, spank.

Article 7: Laws regarding bedtime shall be set by Congress and shall not be changed otherwise.

Article 8: The citizens have their inalienable rights to freedom of speech, religion, pen, pencil, typewriter, and press.

After hearing the first reading of this historic document, I complimented the junior Senator from Maryland and then asked:

"But where is all this 'compensation' coming from? Everybody seems to get compensation for everything."

"Oh," he said, shuffling through his papers, "I guess I forgot to read you Article 9. Here it is: 'The Treasury shall obtain its money by taxes, i.e., income taxes. The Treasury shall pay compensations.'"

"But I'm the only one in the family with any income," I said. "I'll be the only taxpayer."

"I know," he said calmly.

"Well, I thought we would sort of take our compensation in eggs or vegetables or the stuff we grow," I said.

"Are we going to have watermelons?" Larry asked thoughtfully.

"Yes," I said.

"Oh, Daddy," Lynn said sternly, "you know you aren't really going to grow anything in that garden."

"Well, if the pioneers don't get anything to eat, they're going to be in poor shape," I observed. "That's the kind of laws I had in mind—something that would help me get work done. All you've got here is something about how I can't punish anybody and how I have to pay a lot of salaries. Where does it say anything about work?"

"Didn't I get that in?" Larry asked sheepishly.

"No, you didn't."

For the next hour, we engaged in the sort of log-rolling and back-scratching that would have done a southern legislature proud. I introduced a law making it an offense to create a disturbance before 8:30 A.M. Lynn objected to this on the grounds that it would interfere with her early morning roller-skate practice on the front porch. She introduced a law requiring Larry to do the dishes every day. Larry brought in a law making it mandatory for the girls to set and clear the table and I suggested a

[154]

rule to hold each child responsible for keeping his own room clean.

We compromised all along the line: Lynn agreed to vote for my antidisturbance law if I would amend it so that it would cover only Saturdays, Sundays, and holidays, and I voted for her dish-washing law when she changed it so that Larry would have to do them every other day. It took real horse trading all the way, but we finally passed our laws and elected our officers.

At first the whole concept was a mystery to Janie. When we finally made her understand the fundamentals, she was extremely slow in casting her vote, because she insisted on conferring with her dolls about every bill. When she found out that like the others, she was going to have to do some work, she protested.

"Mammas don't have to work," she insisted. "I'm a mamma."

"We all have to work," I said. "You have to work to earn your money."

"But I on'y need a few drops uh money," she pleaded.

Life in a constitutional democracy, particularly the United Toombs of America, can be quite confusing. For the first few days, court was in session almost constantly. Larry loved the legal proceedings and he was like a zealous motorcycle policeman when it came to hauling his sisters before the bar of justice. They retaliated, and the result was that every time one of the girls stepped on Larry's toes, he would file charges and they, in revenge, would demand his arrest whenever he pushed them aside so he could get to the wash basin first.

Then, there were complicated legal problems to be settled. Did freedom of speech mean that Larry could call me an old goat? Did slapping Tonker violate the law against hitting another member of the family? Did freedom of the press give Larry the right to use my typewriter to send a letter of protest to the county commissioners against the condition of our road? And was a five-dollar gift from Lynn's godfather to be considered taxable income? Eventually, it became necessary for me to set aside certain hours on certain days for court business and thus reduce the size of the court's docket.

As for work, I did manage to get the pioneers to do some hard labor. Each of them chose their favorite vegetables and took sole care of them. The household chores were divided up and *done.* I held my breath until I felt sure that the system was working. Finally I relaxed, and then, of course, the thing began to give at the seams.

I discovered that there were weeds that weren't being pulled, pajama bottoms that weren't being picked up, and pans that weren't being scrubbed out. I waited for a couple of bad cases and took them before our court. But then I discovered that public opinion was against me and the offenders were let off with extremely light penalties.

A few days later, the junior Senator called a session of Congress, and without any prior warning to me introduced an amendment to the Constitution. It provided:

"No citizen shall be forced to do involuntary work."

Obviously this amendment had been discussed in advance by the children. They sat there expectantly, waiting to hear what I would have to say. At first, I was ready to put up a stiff argument, but then it occurred to me that this was not the sort of issue that could be settled by words. Either this boy is smarter that I am, I decided, or he isn't—and it's time we found out. So I held my tongue.

"Isn't there any discussion?" asked Larry, bewildered.

"I have nothing to say," I replied.

And so the amendment was passed without a dissenting vote. The next day, I found—as expected—that any work at all was to be considered involuntary.

"I'm not going to work in the garden any more," Larry announced at breakfast.

"No?" I replied casually. "Why not?"

"Too hard."

"It's always hard work to feed yourself."

"You can't make me do it," he said stubbornly. "No involuntary work."

"And I suppose," I said, looking at the girls, "that washing the breakfast dishes is going to come under the head of involuntary work?"

"Well," said Lynn, "I'll do the breakfast dishes for you, but Larry says he isn't going to do dishes any more and I don't think it's fair that we have to do them all. Especially when Janie gets tired after she dries one plate and then goes off to play with her dolls."

"No, that isn't fair. So I guess it will be fair if I do all the work again?"

"Well," she insisted, "washing all the dishes is certainly involuntary work for me."

By now, Larry had gone crabbing and I knew that any minute he would be back with a dozen hard crabs and a request that I pick them out and make him some deviled crab for dinner. Picking crabs is about the most involuntary kind of labor I can think of and I was determined to tell him so. Then I got a bigger and better idea, and for the rest of the day I whistled through the chores.

About ten o'clock the following morning, Lynn knocked on

[157]

the door of my bedroom. In view of the fact that she and her sister had been playing hide and seek around the house since seven, the gentle knock seemed hardly necessary. I told her to come in.

"Are you sick?" she asked.

"No. Why?"

"Well, I just wondered. You're usually up much earlier than this."

Then Larry bustled in to see what was going on.

"Hey," he demanded, "what about breakfast?"

"I don't think I'll fix breakfast this morning."

"Why not?"

"Involuntary work," I said casually. "I just don't feel like cooking any more."

"But what are we going to eat?" he demanded in outraged tones.

"Fix whatever you want," I said amiably.

"Oh boy, oh boy," all three children shouted as they dashed for the kitchen.

I stayed in bed for half an hour and when I heard the front door slam, I got up. The kitchen looked as if it had been struck by a senior-grade tornado. I could understand the burnt toast and spilled cereal, but I'll be darned if I could see how they had worked the orange juice squeezer so as to get all that juice on the ceiling.

When I had finished eating breakfast, I got up from the table and left my dirty dishes—just as they had done. When it was time for lunch, I let them get their own. They opened a can of soup but complained that it didn't taste very good. Since giving out advice came under the heading of involuntary work that day, who was I to tell them that they should have added a can

[158]

of water to the condensed soup? By the time they had finished dirtying the dishes and pans that went into making that lunch, it was just barely possible to walk through the kitchen.

I spent some time that afternoon in the turnip patch. This was my vegetable, since no one else cared much about it. I weeded the patch and picked a mess of greens. I went to the store later and bought two hot dogs and several bottles of milk. By this time, the children had exhausted all the leftovers and ready-cooked items in the house and, unless they wanted milk toast for dinner, I knew they'd have to come to some sort of terms. I went to the kitchen and washed a pan in which to cook the greens and another for the hot dogs. I washed one glass, one plate, one knife, one fork, and one spoon. Then I set one place at the table, by pushing aside enough dirty dishes to make room.

"Gee, don't we get any dinner, either?" asked Larry hungrily.

"I'd be glad to share my turnip greens with you," I said. "And there's plenty of milk."

"No hot dogs?"

"Nope. Just got two for myself. Didn't want to have to carry a lot of involuntary stuff home from the store."

"Gee, Daddy," protested Lynn, "hot dogs don't weigh much."

"I could carry uh hot dog myself," said Janie. "In fac', two."

"Oh, well," I said, "I knew there wouldn't be enough clean dishes, anyway."

While I sat there munching my hot dogs and feeling like the proprietor of a very run-down orphan asylum, the children washed enough dishes for their dinner. I gave them generous helpings of the greens and plenty of milk. I kept my determination strong by reminding myself that they were getting lots

[159]

of vitamins with this meal, and perhaps a little wisdom, whatever the protein content may have been.

"You've *got* to feed us," Larry protested, as he took a third piece of bread and sopped it in pot liquor. "You've *got* to."

"Where does it say that in the Constitution?" I asked.

"Then we'll have to amend the Constitution again," he said.

"If turnip greens is all we gets," Janie observed. "We cert'n'y oughta mend it."

"You can't make me do involuntary work," I reminded him.

Janie started to bed after supper. It took her an extra fifteen minutes to get ready, because all the dolls and all their clothes and furniture were in her bed. When she got to the bottom of the pile, she found one of the kittens. While I watched her struggle with this confusing situation, I almost weakened and did some involuntary labor.

The next morning, I was awakened by the sound of Larry and Lynn in the kitchen. They were engaged in a heated debate.

"This was your big idea," she was saying. "This involuntary work, and I just think you ought to tell him you're sorry. Look at this kitchen. There's not a clean glass to drink orange juice in."

"There's no oranges anyway," he said sadly. "What'll we do?"

"Larry," she said slowly, "we might just as well clean up the mess. You know *he* won't."

They sounded so penitent that I was on the verge of jumping up and helping them. But I had won the struggle—mostly with myself—so far and I decided to wait and see what would happen next. It was half an hour later that my door opened and the procession of children entered. Lynn was carrying a cup of colored water which was supposed to be coffee. Larry was carrying some charred bread which might have been toast.

[160]

"Well, this is a surprise," I said, as if I had just awakened. "Where did you find enough clean dishes?"

"Come and look at the kitchen," said Lynn.

I got up to take a look.

"I washed the dishes," said Larry.

"I dried them," said Lynn.

"And I swept uh floor," said the small fry.

"It's very nice," I said. "And this was voluntary work, wasn't it?"

They smiled happily.

"We're going to clean up our rooms, now," Lynn said.

"And then we thought we'd have a session of Congress," said Larry.

"Another amendment coming up?" I asked amiably.

"Well," he said thoughtfully, "we guessed we'd better repeal that one about involuntary work. It didn't seem to work out so well."

"No," I said, trying to choke down the burnt toast, "no, it didn't."

Chapter Fifteen

I AM a man who appreciates animal life as much as the next guy. I enjoy seeing a dog's tail wagging. I respond to the soft sound of a cat's purr. A hen's triumphant cackle, cutting across the field on a hot summer day, is music to my ears. But this animal thing can be carried too far and, in our case, it was.

Merely owning Tonker was enough to turn a man against animals. He had long, silky ears that flapped in a most engaging way when he ran to greet you. But that was all that could be said for him. For he also had no brains and no inhibitions. It had taken six months of vigorous work just to housebreak him. By then, he had broken my spirit and I decided that there was no use in trying to teach him anything more complicated. As a result, he never learned to keep off the furniture or to stop chewing up toys, clothes, and shoes.

He could snitch a pat of butter off the table while you were walking to the sink with dirty dishes and could swipe a bone out of the refrigerator while you were picking up milk off the top shelf. He still would not come when called, unless it suited his mood, and if you went away from the house, it was almost impossible to leave him behind. He would try all the doors, in his efforts to get out, and if he couldn't find one that was open, he would try all the windows. If he could not push the screen out entirely, he would try to claw a hole in it. But, generally, it was advisable to leave Tonker behind.

The first time I took him to the store, he trotted back into the proprietor's living quarters behind the store, picked a ham bone off the table, and pranced nonchalantly out the front door of the store. The next time I took him, I tied him on the front porch and he chewed through his leash, came in the store, and swiped half a pound of bacon before I spotted him. After that, I made sure he stayed outside, with no leash, in spite of his penchant for sitting down in the middle of the state road to scratch his fleas while speeding cars swerved and screeched around him.

In all of his unconventional conduct, Tonker received Larry's tacit support. It occurred to me, sometimes, that the dog's personality had been shaped by Larry for the real purpose of revolt against me, in some Œdipean sense. Now Dad had just installed new screens on the back windows to replace some that Tonker had worn out, when we set out *without* the dog one day. Tonker dashed about the house, knocking over vases, books, and chairs, desperately looking for an exit. He finally decided to try his strength on one of the new screens. Larry looked back over his shoulder as we walked away from the house to see how Tonker was doing. Suddenly, he cried out admiringly:

"Look, Daddy, at his cute little nose sticking out of the screen."

My father seized a hammer and I could not tell whether he intended to brain the dog or the boy. All he did, finally, was to patch the new hole in the new screen.

[163]

The girls' two cats, on the whole, were better behaved. Except for nights when it was too cold or too rainy outside, they were housebroken. You don't expect so much of a cat, and I came to accept it as natural when, in the midst of dinner, one or both of them would suddenly leap on the table, snatch a drumstick or a pork chop, and disappear. And it seemed perfectly normal to find that they preferred to sleep in the dresser drawer where I kept my white shirts or, if that were closed, on top of my finished manuscript on the desk. With cats in the house I don't believe that it is possible to take a step without tripping over them. By and by I grew accustomed to finding half-eaten mice on the floor of the shower and the feathery remains of a sparrow dinner in the closet. After all, they were just cats, and they purred nicely, even when I woke up at night to find them sleeping on my face.

Somehow, somewhere, sometime, that spring, Lynn had talked me into buying chickens. I got a few hens, a few fryers, and a few baby chicks. They finally produced an egg one morning and Lynn came rushing into announce the great news.

"I hope it's a good one," I said. "As it stands, this egg cost $22.50."

But since the hens *did* lay eggs, I didn't object to the noise they made in the process, even if a great deal of it was to be heard at dawn. Because the little ones fried up so nicely, I didn't mind hauling water to them or even chasing them through the blackberry briars when they got lost.

Sometimes, of course, I felt a little like a man servant to these animals. The question would ask itself again and again: Did I own them, or did they own me? But I could have made out, had it not been for the childrens' bad habit of always trying to expand. We had got the baby chicks at the girls' insistence.

[164]

When Larry learned about this, he decided to get into the act.

"I think the hens would be happier if we had a rooster," he said speculatively.

"We need a rooster in just the same way we need more holes in the head," I said.

"It just doesn't seem like home without a man to run things," he said.

I couldn't put up too much of an argument against this statement, of course, but I still refused to pay out money for a rooster. One day, Larry came home to announce that he had found the rooster he wanted and had made a deal to buy him for a dollar. Furthermore, he had the dollar. Later in the day, Larry came riding home with the rooster on the handlebars of his bicycle —or, it appeared, the rooster came flying to our house with Larry and the bicycle in tow.

Judging by the size of the brute, it must have been part ostrich. And as soon as Larry put it down, the bird chased me up a pine tree. After the rooster took over, I didn't dare go in the chicken run unless I was fully armed, for he would go into action the minute I opened the gate. Furthermore, he woke me every morning just before the sun came up. He did this out of pure spite and for no other reason.

An idiot dog, two unprincipled tomcats, a dozen shaky baby chicks, a dozen and a half noisy hens and pullets, and an anti-social rooster, I decided, were quite enough animals for the children. One night, when they came home from an afternoon of exploring the countryside and informed me that I was in for a surprise, I was almost—but not quite—prepared for them. Just after supper, the children began to shout happily and I looked out in the yard to see a girl riding a pony. She gave all my children a ride. But when the kids began to hint that they

[165]

could have the pony for the asking, I was distinctly unenthusiastic and managed to discourage the idea.

After this, I thought that I had the situation well in hand. But then Shep appeared. Almost every day we would be visited by some stray dog, who would sniff around for a time and then depart. So I paid no attention to this shaggy collie when he first trotted across from the mainland. He sat himself down as if he had always lived around the place and remained until late in the day. Before I realized what was happening, Lynn was out in the yard feeding him. This was the original mistake, because it appeared that eating was a luxury to which Shep was unaccustomed. Having found food at our house, he decided to stay and the next morning I awoke to find him digging up the neighbor's flower bed. They started chucking oyster shells at him to drive him away, but Shep merely got out of range and sat down. Then, he came back over to our yard. I didn't want to encourage the children in unkindness to animals, so I couldn't take any overt action against the dog. But I did try to indicate, politely but firmly, that Shep should go back where he came from. He was impervious to such discouragement—especially since my girls kept slipping him more food.

At last I ordered his supply of food cut off, telling the children that he would get tired of hanging around and would go away. In the course of my lifetime I have been wrong about many things—but never quite so wrong as I was in this supposition. When we quit feeding him, Shep just disappeared for a few hours a day. He would forage around the countryside and then come back.

The real reason I objected to him was that he had established himself as the social director of our life. He would determine in a most arbitrary fashion which visitors should be permitted

[166]

in our yard and which should be chased up a tree. He carried on a Hatfield feud with the people next door, snapping and snarling whenever they set foot on our place—and sometimes when they set foot on their own. He followed us everywhere, whether we went out in the boat or set out in Dad's automobile. The only trouble was, he always followed us back.

After a couple of weeks of this, I ordered Larry to search the countryside and find out whom this monster had been haunting before he picked on us. Larry finally ascertained that Shep belonged to a family of sharecroppers who lived a couple of miles away.

"Fine," I said firmly. "Put a rope around his neck, get on your bike, and take him home."

When Shep was out of sight, I felt as if I had lost an aching tooth. The neighbors smiled happily when I told them the news and we enjoyed our freedom while it lasted. This was not long, for in half an hour Shep returned. He crawled under the front porch and went to sleep. Five minutes later, Larry puffed into the yard.

"Well, I gave him back," he said, somewhat sadly.

"That's great," I said. "He beat you home by five minutes."

Larry said he was too tired to take the dog back just then, but promised he would return him the next day. When he tried again, Larry managed to reach the house five minutes before Shep came back. But Shep was no more stubborn than I. The neighbors are nice people and I did not relish the idea of having Shep turn them into hamburger. Furthermore, I was determined that no stray collie was going to screen visitors for me. So, every day for a couple of weeks, I sent Larry up the road with the dog and, every day, the dog would break away and come back. I figured that sooner or later one or the other of us was going to get tired of this—and it just might be Shep. Finally, one week end I put the dog in Dad's car and took him back to his owners myself.

"Tie him up with some heavy rope," I told them. "You better keep him home or I'm liable to shoot him."

Janie listened to this injunction with wide eyes. Then she laughed and said:

"Aw, Daddy, you haven't got uh gun, even."

This time, we enjoyed forty-eight hours of existence without Shep. People around the creek began to be friendly again. The gas man, who had suspended deliveries, promised to bring us a new tank and the electric company said they would send a man in to read the meter and promised not to shut off the service after all. The gas man had just arrived and was walking toward the house when I heard a loud crashing sound in the brush, and there was Shep.

Around the dog's neck was a piece of rope about ten feet long and an inch thick. It had apparently taken him two full days of steady effort to chew through the rope, but he had made it finally and had managed to arrive at just the psychological moment. He started for the gas man, as usual. I grabbed the man, to keep him from fleeing, and Larry grabbed the dog. I started Larry out with him immediately and it wasn't until two or three days later, at 3:00 A.M., that I was awakened by the sound of Shep howling outside the door. At this point, we were all ready to concede defeat and let Shep stay—and I might have, had it not been for the ducks.

A number of people around our creek raised mallard ducks. Larry, for some time, had been trying to get my permission to acquire a few specimens. I told him that it would take just one quack from a duck in our yard to put me right in a straitjacket.

I don't know whether this argument convinced Larry to get the ducks, but I do know that I was crabbing in the river a few days later when he came home on his bicycle.

"Hey, Daddy," he called to me, "the Smiths just gave me a pair of ducks."

There was a large wicker basket perched on the handle bars of the bike and a smile to match on his face. I should have ordered him to return the ducks forthwith, but somehow I couldn't do it. So I merely asked what he expected to do with the ducks.

"Put them in with the chickens," he said. "They're just little, but when they grow up, we can have lots of little ducks. This is a male and a female."

"Okay. Just so I don't have to bother with them," I said sadly.

I needed one more soft crab to have enough for dinner, so I went on searching about in the seaweed. When I finally got to the house, I realized that lunch was very late and I started in a great frenzy to make sandwiches. Just then, Larry came huffing and puffing into the house, crying loud alarm.

"One of the ducks got loose," he told me.

"Great," I said. "Now we only have to worry about one duck."

"But Daddy, what good is one duck? We won't be able to hatch little ones."

"That's what I was thinking."

But Larry was taking his loss seriously and I could not resist his entreaties to help him pursue the lost bird. So, putting some lunch on the table for the girls, I set forth, with an empty stomach, to help Larry chase a duck. The critter had headed straight for the fringe of swampy land along the edge of the creek. I sent Larry out into the creek in a rowboat and walked into the high grass of the marsh. Just ahead of me, I could see the grass rustling, so I started to dash for the place where I was sure I would find the duck.

I did not dash far, because after about two steps, I fell in a hole and landed flat on my face in the mud. Picking myself up and still seeing the rustling, I started toward it slowly. This time, I sank in mud up to my knees. On and on I struggled, in and out of mud holes, until I reached the spot where the grass was moving. And what should I find there, but the ever-loving Shep! He had decided to join the game, and before I had a chance to take aim and kick him in the slats, I saw the grass moving somewhere else. But this time I had stood still long enough to sink in the mud almost to my waist. When I got loose, I started off again.

This time, it *was* the duck, but by the time I got to his refuge, he had moved on. The neighbors and one of the rivermen who lived across the creek had joined us now. But, seeing me covered with black mud from head to toe, they wisely stayed on the bank and bossed the operation. For the next half hour, the duck and I played tag through the swamp while the onlookers shouted orders to me. The duck managed to maintain a good lead, largely because I was carrying so much excess weight in the form of swamp mud. Then too, I was crippled by the scratches I had suffered. I was hungry, the summer sun was beating down like an acetylene torch, and I was about ready to give up the whole thing. The duck apparently reached the same conclusion at the same time, for just as I sat down on top of a clump of swamp grass, he squatted down in a clearing—just waiting for me to come after him. Someone on shore told me where he was, and, summoning one final ounce of strength, I started to sneak up on him.

[170]

His back was turned toward me and I crept to within a few feet of him. Cautiously, I raised the crab net I was carrying and made ready for the final lunge. Just then, like a streak of lightning, Shep—that faithful nuisance—pounced. He seized the duck by the neck, trotted up on the bank and sat down. He sat there proudly, the duck at his feet, and waited for me to get on solid ground and praise him. I rushed up to him and snatched the bird away, cradling it in my arms, like a vaudeville baritone who has at last found Chloë. The duck opened its eyes, gave me one reproachful look, and then died of the broken neck inflicted by Shep.

That mutt was sitting at my feet, waiting to see how I was going to take it.

"Shep!" I screamed. There was something about my tone of voice, I guess, that gave him the idea that he wasn't wanted, because he took off as if he had a string of firecrackers tied to his tail.

When I had wiped away the tears the children shed for the late, departed duck, I sent Larry out to make sure that Shep had gone as far as it looked as if he were going. Larry reported back later to say that he had overtaken Shep about half-way home and had escorted him the rest of the way. This time, his owners put a chain on him.

I felt that all this trouble might have been worth while if Shep were really gone. The children felt bad about the whole thing and even worse, three or four days later, when the rooster did in the other duck. I heaved a secret sigh of relief, however, and settled back to try to enjoy life with only one dog, two cats, one rooster, thirty chickens, no ducks, and no Shep.

The next day, I glanced up from my sandwich-making at

lunch time when I heard a shout from Larry. I walked outside and found him astride that pony again and holding a wicker basket across his legs.

"Hey, Daddy," he said happily, "I got two new ducks."

"To say the least," I observed. "What's that you're riding?"

"They said I could have *him*, too, if you'd let me."

I looked at him coldly.

"Well, I won't."

"Aw, Daddy."

"And when you take the pony back, you can just drop off those two ducks. Tell the people that we'd be glad to have them—when they are full grown and ready for the roasting pan."

"Aw, Daddy."

"Get, now," I told him, in what I hoped was the same tone of voice that had driven away old Shep.

Larry turned the pony around and disappeared down the road. When I could see him no longer, I started to walk back to the house. Just then I heard the rattle of a chain. I rolled my eyes toward the sky and, without looking, knew only too well what it was that fate had brought back to my doorstep.

"Shep," I said slowly, turning now in the direction from which the noise had come, "Shep, if you want to stay here badly enough to chew up a chain, I guess there's not much I can do about it."

He wagged his tail in agreement.

Chapter Sixteen

THERE was one thing about my children—they were enthusiasts. Or, perhaps I should say with more accuracy that when they got interested in a subject, they knew no limits. When they weren't interested, they could also be completely disinterested. This was the way it was with the garden—both ways, that is.

As hardy pioneers, we started out to raise a whopping garden. But the children found the going rough and soon became vastly disinterested—all except Janie, who was "taking care" of the corn and the okra—vegetables that she seemed to be able to eat in any given quantity. Larry and Lynn could not have cared less about the whole business. I made them stick at it, though, until long after we had passed the point of diminishing returns —that being when I had to do more work to make them work than if I had done it myself. It was when the corn and okra were ready to harvest that I decided I had better make a change. Janie, who had toiled hard to raise her crop, came to me tearfully to complain.

" 'Ere's okry and corn, but it's too high for me to reach," she said.

I studied the situation and found that the vegetables had, indeed, grown too tall for her to reach. This seemed to be a good excuse, so I told her I would take them over, with her assistance. I transferred Larry from gardening to taking care of the chickens and shifted Lynn back to housework. This left me with the entire garden to care for, and it was at this point that the children became all-out enthusiasts—about raising things.

Now that I was going to do the labor, it seemed to them that we should try to raise everything. Lynn brought home some red cabbage plants donated by a kindly neighbor. Janie picked up a few zinnias. Larry lugged home fifty sweet potato plants. None of this worried me too much—I was glad to see the youngsters taking an interest in the place—until, one day, Larry came home with twelve raspberry plants, Lynn with a small black walnut tree, and the little girl with numerous sprigs of mint all at the same time! I, of course, was supposed to set out this stuff.

"This is fine and dandy," I said. "But I've got just about as much as I can take care of now. Will you kindly quit trying to break my back?"

This plea stopped importations for a few days, but finally Larry came home in a state of excitement with some tomato plants.

"We've got plenty of tomatoes," I said, in exasperation.

"But not like these," he said happily. "These are little yellow tomatoes."

I grumbled and muttered and threatened to throw the plants to the chickens, but finally, at sundown, I set them out. Larry watched me, and when we got back to the house he confronted Lynn in triumph and said:

"Okay, pay me. He set them out."

"What's this all about?" I asked.

"I bet him a nickel that you wouldn't plant those, if he brought them home," she said sadly. "You said you wouldn't the other day."

"Well," I excused myself lamely, "I didn't like to see them go to waste. But nothing else—understand?"

They nodded solemnly.

I stuck with the garden bravely during the days of its growing pains. I hilled the potatoes, staked the tomatoes, and put up poles for the beans. I thinned out the carrots, cultivated the corn, and mulched the broccoli. Then I suddenly found that I had so much else to do that I just couldn't work in the garden any more. Mother Earth began to yield abundantly—all the things the kids had dragged home and all the things that Dad had planted for us.

The trouble now was that I didn't have time enough to pick the things that hung from the vines. And whenever I started out to the garden to gather a basket of tomatoes, on the theory that I would put up some tomato juice, I encountered four or five more critical problems along the way. I managed to pick the few things that we needed for the table, but this hardly made a dent in the crop. Soon we had so many green peppers hanging on the plants that they were dragging the ground; our unpicked cucumbers were turning yellow; and our tomato patch was rich with the odor of fermenting fruit.

Then garden pests, attracted by the tastiest feast which had been available to them in some years, began to converge on the garden. Every turtle and rabbit in southern Maryland made straight for the tomato plants. Beetles, borers, and aphids converged on the front garden. The back garden was full of things that crawled, things that flew, and things that swam. Medium-sized bugs, big bugs, and huge bugs decended upon us in

[175]

swarms and hordes. It looked as if my harvesting problem was going to be solved for me, to the extent that there wouldn't be anything left for us at all.

So I took time out and went after the pests with sprays and bait and reduced their number considerably. But there was one beetle, eating my broccoli and cauliflower, which seemed impervious to all known poisons. The only way to kill this nuisance was to pick it off and drop it in a can of kerosene. One morning, I offered the children a penny for each beetle they picked for me. Half an hour later, Lynn burst into the house and said happily:

"Boy, this is a good job."

"Are they easy for you to find?" I asked.

"We've got more than three hundred already. How much do we get for that many?"

"What?" I screamed. "That's three dollars! I could buy a year's supply of cauliflower for three dollars."

So I hastily devalued the beetle exchange rate—fixing it at ten beetles for a penny, or twenty-five cents for three hundred. Still, whenever the children needed any spending money, they just strolled out into the garden and spent a few minutes picking the first three hundred beetles they met. My bank roll suffered and grew smaller, but the beetle population never seemed to drop.

The beetles took care of the surplus broccoli and cauliflower. Blight did in the cucumbers and cantaloupes. Borers got the squash and turtles ate the tomatoes. After a while, the beans got tired of bearing vegetables I didn't pick. I used what I could and gave away all that anyone would take. The chickens got the rest, and I'd go through the garden when I had the chance and clear paths through the mounds of vegetables, for fear that I'd

[176]

wake up some morning to find that we were completely isolated from the outside world by a wall of rotting vegetation.

Before I had finally put a stop to it, the children had imported a sample of everything that would grow in our part of the country—except for one thing. A man down the road owned a lime tree, a most improbable bit of tropical vegetation to find in Maryland. But the tree did grow, and every time Larry passed it he would think of a new argument in favor of growing limes. Under the circumstances, I couldn't get the least bit interested in anything that grew. But one day Larry came home in a state of wild excitement. The people who owned the lime tree were moving, he told me, and had said he could have the tree.

I was deeply engrossed, at the moment, in the preparation of a plum flummery which I hoped would somewhat reduce the surplus of plums. So I said absent-mindedly:

"Okay. You can have it."

He went away happily and I forgot the whole matter. A few days later, I was walking to the store and passed the home of the man who owned the lime tree. He called to me from the yard.

"Say," he said, irritably, "when are you going to get that darn tree out of here? The people who are moving in say they don't want it."

"Tree?" I asked innocently. "What tree?"

"The lime tree," he said insistently. "Larry promised you'd be down to dig it up."

"Larry did? Oh, sure, I'll send him down this afternoon."

"Pretty big job for the little boy," he said. "And I'm too busy to help him."

He gave me a look showing that he'd heard how I kept the

[177]

children working in the fields all day in the hot sun while I sat on the front porch and sipped juleps.

"Oh, I'll help him, of course," I said hastily.

"We're moving day after tomorrow," he said darkly.

"We'll be down this evening," I assured him, finally.

That afternoon, something went wrong. I can't remember whether it was the day that Janie got her hair full of roofing tar or whether that was the day Shep chased the children's Sunday School superintendent up the big pear tree. The poor man was up there for fifteen minutes before we decided that Shep wasn't barking at the possum that lived in the tree. Anyway, I got badly off schedule and it wasn't until nearly five o'clock that I extricated myself from the day's crises long enough to go with Larry to dig up the neighbor's lime tree.

Until then I had never made the acquaintance of a lime tree —but from the moment I approached it, I was able to claim a blood relationship with the citrus family. For the tree was covered with cleverly hidden spikes, about two inches long and sharp as needles. It was not possible to approach the tree from any angle without impaling yourself. Before I had finished studying the thing, to decide how we should go about uprooting it, I was breached in a number of places and leaking badly. It wasn't such a big tree—not much taller than I. But the struggle would have been more even had I thought to wrap myself in barbed wire. Finally I decided that if could dig up all the roots, the tree would have to topple. Then I could put a rope around the blasted thing and drag it down the road, since it was patently impossible to grip it anywhere. So, manfully I started to dig.

It was hot that day and the lime tree had a root system that reached in all directions. After half an hour, I was ready to chuck the whole show. The children were getting hungry. I looked around to see if I could sneak away, but the owner was standing on the porch, tapping his foot impatiently and watching my every move. So I dug and dug and dug. I followed those roots down into the bowels of the earth—through rock, water, sand, and something that looked like iron ore. Gradually, the excavation spread and deepened until I was afraid that the man's house was going to topple into it. I had dug up practically his entire front yard before the tree even began to lean a little, but I was in worse shape, for I was leaning a lot and, while the tree was dripping blood—mine, of course—I was sweating lime juice.

The tree's owner had his supper out on the front porch, where he could keep an eye on me. My children were half-starved now and whining for their own supper, which was long overdue. But I carried on grimly, digging and digging and sweating and sweating. Finally, the tree toppled—right on top of me, of course. I went down with a crash, like a monarch of the forest, and landed on Larry. By the time they got a rope on the tree and pulled it off me, you could see daylight through every square inch of my hide. Then I started to tug on the rope, figuring that if the kids and I got enough of a head start, we could get away without filling the crater in the man's front yard. But he had anticipated this maneuver, and just as I got the tree moving, I heard him clear his throat. I looked back to see him standing on the edge of the excavation.

"It would make a nice swimming pool," I suggested cheerfully.

But he was not impressed with the idea.

"Just dig a couple more feet and you'll find coal, I'm sure," I said. "That hole would make a fine mine entrance."

"There's an oil furnace in the house already," he said sourly.

"*Well*," I said, and commenced filling in the hole. The moon had risen before I had finished and started dragging the tree home. I only had a short rope, and so every time I took a step, the tree would creep up behind me and jab me in the rump. But I was too weary to move any faster.

"Boy," said Larry when we got home, "now we can have our own limes."

"I'd better get a blood count on that tree," I said. "I've got an idea that we might be able to sell the limes to a blood bank."

Then I started in the house to fix supper.

"Hey," said Larry. "Aren't you going to plant it?"

"Who, me?" I asked testily. "I dug it up, isn't that enough?"

It seemed to me, when I thought it over later, that I was being a little unreasonable. But now I decided to wait and see whether Larry would at least start to plant the tree himself. If he did I had decided to help him. I didn't want him to get the idea I would do all his work for him. There was no telling how much stuff he might bring home, then.

But next day Larry made no gesture toward planting the tree. Every time I passed the hateful thing and saw its leaves wilting, I thought of all the agony I had gone through. That night, after the children were in bed, I decided that I would suffer more if the tree just lay there and died than I would if I planted it. So, by the light of a full moon, I dug a hole and stuck the darn thing in.

The next morning I slept later than usual and Larry came in to awaken me.

"Hey, Daddy," he asked, "who planted the lime tree?"

"Lime tree?" I said.

"Yeah. I wonder who could of done it."

"The gremlins, maybe," I suggested.

[180]

He rushed into Lynn's room and I heard him whisper excitedly.

"He did it. He did it."

Lynn groaned, and then I heard no more. Just as I was putting breakfast on the table, she came to me sorrowfully and asked:

"Could I have a nickel of my next week's allowance?"

"What for?" I replied.

"I owe it to Larry. I lost another bet on you."

Chapter Seventeen

WHILE we were away during the winter, Dad had been busy changing the interior of the house. He had shifted a partition here and a wall there and, when he finished, he discovered that there was no kitchen in the house. There was a little cubbyhole left over which, by a peculiar coincidence, had a couple of pipe connections coming through the wall, so he decided to put the kitchen there. But there wasn't room enough for the refrigerator, and so that went out on the back porch. He located the sink and work tables on one end of the room, but the dishes and the stove were on the other end. Then he suddenly discovered that in changing the house, he had left out the back door again. This was the door he was always moving around, and it was bound to get lost, sooner or later. When he discovered the mistake, he decided that the only place he could put the door was in the kitchen.

Thus it was that I found the main stream of traffic, which at certain times of the day was pretty heavy, moving directly through my kitchen. It passed right down the center of the room, between the sink and the stove. As a result, I would keep bumping into people while I was cooking a meal—people riding bicycles, walking on their hands, or carrying loads of bricks through the kitchen. I would turn away from the stove with a kettle of cooked vegetables and start for the sink—only to find that Dad was walking through the room with a ladder so long that, by the time he got out of the way, the vegetables would be cold. Sometimes, I got caught on the sink side of the kitchen and watched dinner burn on the stove while Dad and Larry wrestled a twenty-foot length of pipe out the back door.

At one time or another, I fell into most of the traps which were set for me in this kitchen. But one day I fell into all of them. This was on Lynn's birthday—a sort of culinary Pearl Harbor for me. I had been awakened early that morning by the sound of old Shep returning from one of his periods of exile, clanking his chain behind him. I couldn't get back to sleep because that antisocial rooster began to crow.

Lynn had invited two or three friends over for ice cream and cake that afternoon, so I set about manfully to manufacture same. It was a hot day and I was dressed in my tropical cooking uniform—a pair of trunks and nothing else. While I was making the ice cream, Larry disappeared from the house. He was opposed, as a matter of principle, to Lynn's birthday. His gesture of protest was to go out in the river and catch a bucket of big hard crabs, which he dragged in just as I was putting the cake in the oven.

"How about some devilled crab, Pop?" he asked, trying to start an argument.

"Put them down by the stove," I said. "I'll steam them when I get a chance."

I chased him out of the kitchen and, while the cake was baking, started to look up some recipes for icing. As all this was going on, the girls came racing through the kitchen, with Larry in hot pursuit, traveling U.S. Route 1 toward the back door.

This buffalo stampede went around the house and through the kitchen two or three more times while the cake was in the oven. When I finally peeked at it, I discovered that one layer had developed a serious sag.

Having decided on a seven-minute frosting for the cake, I took my stance in front of the double boiler and let it get up steam. Then I started turning the egg beater for that interminable seven minutes. About two minutes later, a cat streaked through the kitchen, passing between me and the stove and leaving a pattern of claw marks on the top of my bare feet. Right behind him came another cat, also trampling my feet, and, on the same path, Shep followed. The dog, moving at top speed, very nearly knocked me over—and did succeed in upsetting the bucket of hard crabs. It was then that I found myself completely surrounded by a couple of dozen of enraged, snapping hard crabs.

Now I doubt if there are many people who have found themselves in a hot kitchen, three minutes along on beating a seven-minute icing, barefooted and practically engulfed by hard crabs on a rampage. There was certainly nothing in my previous training in life which had equipped me to cope with such a situation. As I saw it, the choice lay between the frosting and my toes. I chose the latter. Dropping the egg beater, I jumped on a table and began to yell for the kids. But, bless their little hearts, they had decided at last to go off somewhere and let their old daddy finish making his cake in peace.

There was a broom within reach, and with this I was able to clear a path through the carpet of crabs. With most of them rounded up, I made my way back to the stove, where my icing was well on the road to ruin, and began to turn the egg beater again. Just as I got up steam, I felt a fugitive crab crawl across my foot. I had to stop and corral him. By the time I got back to the frosting, I had no idea whether it had been cooking for seven, seventeen, or seventy minutes. But I kept on beating. Every time I got the water boiling hard and the beater spinning fast, another crab would sneak out from under the stove and take a swing at my big toe. Then I'd have to stop and do battle with him.

The frosting just wouldn't get stiff enough and I finally quit. It occurred to me that it might harden up if I put it in the refrigerator, so I began to slap it on the cake. To compensate for the sag in the bottom layer, I put a lot of frosting in to fill up the gap. Then I went whistling off after a couple of crabs I had seen headed for the living room.

An hour later, I looked in the refrigerator to see how the cake was doing. It was on one of the top shelves, near the freezing unit, and putting it there had been one of the worst mistakes of the whole day. For the icing I had piled up between the layers to make up for the low spot had merely served as a lubricant. The top layer slid downhill, slipped off the edge of the plate, and was hanging there like a Frenchman's beret. There really wasn't much frosting left on the cake—but there was plenty of it in the icebox. I had broccoli with icing, bacon with icing, and a piece of left over roast beef with more icing on it than the cake. I managed to repair the cake in time for the festivities, but it was days before I got the last of that gooey frosting mopped up.

By and large, our kitchen utensils were war surplus—Spanish-American war, that is. There were lots of lids and lots of pans, but none of the lids fitted any of the pans. There were tops to double boilers and bottoms to double boilers, but none matched.

[186]

The saucepans had grown so round on the bottom, from years of use, that they lolled about on the stove like roly-poly dolls. In the bottom of the kitchen closet, there were cooking devices so antique that I could not identify them with any certainty.

One night, when my electric waffle iron broke down, I tried to use a waffle iron I found in the closet. It had apparently been invented before the days of Edison, for it worked on the gas stove. It took me about fifteen minutes to cook the first waffle and then I found it was stuck to the griddle. Another fifteen minutes went into getting it scraped out, and now I thought I would try again. This time I cut my time down to ten minutes for cooking and ten minutes for scraping out. By the time I finally got a waffle cooked, the kids had filled up on salad and bread and syrup and had gone out to play.

Of course, I was just the right guy to work in a setup like this. There was nothing, absolutely nothing, about the way I operated a kitchen which would have earned the approval of a Home Economics teacher—except, possibly, the results. I didn't plan my meals. I just stumbled on them. Since there were no stores nearby which stocked anything fancier than canned goods, I had to depend upon the garden for our fresh produce. About four o'clock in the afternoon, I would begin to think about dinner. I would hurry out to the garden to see what was ripe.

If I found that the beetles, in their haste, had spared enough broccoli for a meal, I would rush to the hen house to see if there were three eggs. If so, we would have broccoli with hollandaise sauce. Otherwise, I had to start shopping around for something else. When I had pulled enough carrots or picked enough beans for the meal, I began to wonder about dessert. This lead me to the orchard, usually. If I found some ripe pears, I would go back in the house to see if there were some gingerbread mix and

[187]

enough brown sugar to permit me to make an upside-down cake.

We had to take the vegetables as they came. Sometimes it was all squash and string beans. Sometimes it was nothing but tomatoes, green peppers, okra, and onions. I cooked one of these each day and then, on the fifth day, mixed them all together in a pot-pouri.

When my father came down on Friday night, he brought meat from town. This lasted over the week end, and after that I was on my own. My food budget permitted me to buy a few hot dogs or a little ham at the country store, but sooner or later every week I ran out of money and, consequently, out of meat. Then I would take to the river in search of crabs, humming a little tune with words that went like this:

> *It's the end of the week*
> *And we haven't any money.*
> *If I don't catch some crabs*
> *We'll eat macaroni.*

The crabs were well acquainted with my routine. On Monday, Tuesday, and Wednesday they knew I had enough meat. So they would loaf around in the shallow water in front of my house, taking sun baths, smoking big cigars and blowing smoke rings my way. But on Thursday and Friday, they would go into hiding to such an extent that every once in a while we did have macaroni. But one Friday, they got extremely careless and I caught enough to make a dinner and have some left over for the week end, too.

Later that day, I heard Shep's war cry and hurried out to see who was being rended limb from limb. It turned out to be a couple of local fishermen on the beach, hauling in their nets. I

[188]

called Shep off, and the fishermen, out of gratitude to me for having saved their legs for future use, left us a mess of perch.

That night, Dad came down with a pork roast and I put it in the refrigerator. My father is a hard man to please —when you're cooking for him. He will eat whatever you serve, but if it's something he doesn't like, he assumes the faintly pained expression of royalty eating a soggy sandwich at a palace servants' ball. The only sure way to please him is to serve something raised on the premises or fished out of the river. No matter what it tastes like, he enjoys it. So I decided that he would be happier with fish and crabs to eat over the week end and I would leave the pork roast for future reference. On Monday I planned to have the roast for dinner, and late in the afternoon I fished it out of the refrigerator. Ever since our brush with ptomaine in Florida, things that had been in the refrigerator for more than twenty-four hours made me as suspicious as the house dick in a bachelor hotel. I had rather forgotten about this roast, or else I would have cooked it and then put it back on ice. So I sniffed it carefully now and I thought that it seemed a little over-ripe.

Then I started toward the door to throw it to the dogs. But I began to wonder. Didn't I just imagine that it smelled funny? Maybe, I thought, I'm being too hasty about this. After all, this hunk of meat cost me better than four dollars. In the end, I decided not to throw it away, but to cook it and try a sample. So I roasted it thoroughly and just before dinner cut off a piece. It tasted fine and, outside the kitchen door, I saw old Shep eyeing me hungrily.

"If I'm going to the Great Beyond, I'm going to take you with me," I said, tossing him a bone out of the roast.

My faith in the piece of meat was completely restored now, and so I went ahead with the rest of the meal. But just as I was

[189]

about to set it on the table, I looked out of the back door and espied Shep rolling around on the ground. He gave every appearance of being in mortal agony. In a panic, I put my hand on my stomach, expecting to stir up a swarm of stabbing pains. But nothing happened. I looked at Shep again. He was leaning up against a tree and his body seemed to be shaking. Then he staggered out of sight. Again, I felt my stomach anxiously, but there was no reaction.

"I guess dogs feel it quicker," I told myself.

Hearing the children coming, I shoved the roast into the oven to get it out of sight and opened a can of salmon—which seemed to be the easiest available substitute. I made a salad— racing against the moment when I expected to start rolling around like the dog—and put it on the table.

"Aren't you eating, Daddy?" asked Lynn, when I didn't set a place for myself.

"No," I replied. "I don't think I'm feeling well."

"You don't *think* you're feeling well," observed Larry. "Don't you know?"

It was too much trouble to try to explain my predicament, so I just stretched out on the couch and assumed the sweet, patient expression which I wanted the children to have as a last memory of me. But as the evening wore on, I experienced none of the expected pains. The only thing that happened was that I got terribly hungry. It seemed to me that I might as well die on a full stomach as with an empty one, so I made some sandwiches and then went to bed. I was tired, but I was afraid to sleep. So I got up and made some coffee, so as to be awake when it hit me. Midnight came, and there was still nothing wrong. Finally I decided to take a long chance and go to sleep.

The next morning I felt fine—except for being very sleepy.

[190]

When I got up to fix breakfast, I came face to face with the roast. I resolved to throw it away after breakfast, but then I began to wonder again.

"Any of you children seen Shep this morning?" I asked.

"Sure," said Janie, " 'ere he is, waitin' for his brefesk."

He was there and I was wondering how he had managed to survive when Lynn asked:

"Did you give him a bone yesterday, Daddy?"

"Yes. Why?"

"Well, it must have caught in his throat. He was choking something awful, and when I hit him, he caughed it up."

That settled my last doubt about the roast and so I put it in the icebox and figured that dinner was taken care of that day, anyway. Late in the afternoon, I heard a car in the yard and went out to find an old friend of mine from Washington. He came in for a visit and after a time I asked:

"Why don't you stay for dinner?"

"Who's doing the cooking?" he asked suspiciously.

"I am."

"What are you having? Are you sure I won't get poisoned?" he asked, laughing.

"Po—" I started to say, but caught myself just in time. Then I remembered that I had some frozen hamburger in the tray of the icebox and I got it out. I put it on the stove to thaw and went back to tell my friend that we would have meat loaf.

"Okay. I'll take a chance and eat your cooking," he said. "But the last time I ate a man's cooking, I got sick. Fellow gave me some bad pork."

In a little while, I went out to the kitchen to see if the hamburger had thawed out. It had—in fact, it had evaporated. I found two fat cats and Tonker polishing off the last of it. That

[191]

left me with nothing *but* the pork roast and, my friend's suspicions to the contrary, I determined to serve it. When I put it on the table, he looked at it thoughtfully.

"Funny-looking meat loaf," he said.

"Changed my mind," I said.

It was a good dinner, I must say. That piece of meat was the most thoroughly cooked pork seen since the fire in the Chicago stockyards. It was crisp and brown on the outside and flaky inside. I served homemade applesauce with it, along with green beans out of the garden and some of our sweet potatoes. For dessert, we had a blackberry cobbler, made with some home-picked berries I had canned. When Larry had finished, he smacked his lips happily and said:

"Gee, that was good."

"Yes," said my friend. "I'll have to take back what I said about men cooks."

I beamed happily.

"Was that the piece of pork Granddad brought down last week?" Larry asked.

I tried to flash him the storm signal, but he wouldn't be stopped.

"I thought it smelled funny in the refrigerator," he said, as he left the table, "but it sure tasted all right."

I looked quickly at my friend. He was turning green and a few minutes later, he left. We had a couple more good meals off that roast, without any ill effects. I don't know how my friend felt, because, come to think of it, I've never heard from him since.

Chapter Eighteen

ONE summer evening after supper, the children dashed out of the house to work on some project that Larry had conjured up. I had some apple jelly to make and pushed the dishes aside until later. I heard the youngsters talking together happily out by the tool house, so I decided to let them play for a little while longer. I finished the jelly, stacked up the dishes, and put some water on to heat. Then I discovered that our water system, which sometimes stopped functioning for no apparent cause, had suffered a lapse. Since I couldn't go ahead with dish washing, I decided I would round up the children and get the little girls ready for bed.

When I reached the tool house, I found that the project which had been keeping them so happy involved painting an old wagon belonging to Larry. They had managed to get some of the paint on the wagon, but not as much as they had smeared on each other. All of them were daubed with five colors, from head to foot. This was so routine that I hardly ever got mad at them. A few minutes of peace and quiet, when there are children around, is always purchased at some kind of price. So I got a rag and some turpentine and went to work on them. It was necessary to take off what few clothes they were wearing, and when I loosened up the paint, I told them to go take a shower. Just then, I remembered that the water was off in the house.

"Go on down and jump in the river," I said. "You'll get rid of most of it that way and I'll finish you up with the water I was heating for the dishes."

They raced off, bare as three plucked chickens, and a few minutes later I heard them whooping and yelling around on the lawn of the house next door. I glanced over and saw my three naked and gaudily painted children running around a group of ladies who were dressed in white summer clothes. I had not realized that the neighbors were entertaining and they, I knew, had not been expecting the entertainment which was now being provided.

"Wahooo!" Larry was shouting. "Me Big Chief Running Wolf."

The three children were doing a war dance around the group of visitors.

"Me little fat baby caboose," Janie cried, making a dash for the snowy white lap of the lady who lived next door.

I let out a war whoop myself and the children, hearing me, dashed for the river. I was too covered with paint and apple jelly to go over immediately and make my peace with the visitors, so I went in the house to clean up a little. Then I went over and somehow got involved in a conversation from which it was impossible to extricate myself. Meanwhile, the sun had gone down and the moon was rising and the children were still swimming around. I could tell that some of the ladies did not think too highly of my method of raising youngsters.

Living as we were, the children had lost most of the inhi-

bitions which city life had built up in them. People around the countryside looked upon us as eccentric, and the children tried their best to live up to this reputation. I was not entirely happy about the direction in which we were moving. Next to raising children to be little prigs, I can't think of anything worse than raising them to be little Characters.

"Children," I said at dinner the next day, "sometime, we are all going to have to go back to Civilization, ugh! And you're going to have to learn that under certain circumstances human beings are supposed to act like human beings."

They looked at me with obvious interest, so I continued:

"Now, you guys have gotten into the habit of doing anything that comes to mind. People around here are getting to think that we're funny people. We've got to act more like other people do when we're out. We've got to learn to know people around here and get used to being out in polite society. After all, the world is full of people and you must be able to get along with them. We've got to learn to be respectable, when we have to. I don't know what your relatives will think . . ."

"Daddy, you better start shaving then," said Lynn.

"All right, I'll shave tomorrow."

"And quit riding the bicycle to the store in your bare feet," said Larry.

"I will if you'll quit getting in political arguments down there," I said. "People think you're awful sassy."

The first step in my campaign to convert the children into respected members of the brotherhood of man was to clean them up a few days later and take them calling. I decided I would start at the top of the local social strata, so we went to see some friends of my father's who lived a few miles away.

[196]

They were wealthy people with a huge house which had been in the family since colonial days. I dressed the children up, even forcing them into shoes, and slipped on some natty sports clothes myself.

"Anybody who doesn't act like a lady or gentleman is going to get slugged," I warned them, as we pulled up in the driveway of the place.

Everything went nicely for the first half hour. This was strictly a broad A outfit and I was pleased to see that the children had clung to a few good manners. We were sitting on the front porch, looking out over the river and admiring the roses which grew at the foot of the white porch columns. I felt that we were passing our first test very nicely.

There was a ragged colored man working in the rose garden. From time to time, he looked at me curiously and finally he came up on the porch to get some instructions from the lady of the house. As he was about to leave, he turned to me and said:

"Hi'ya, Alf'ud."

I looked at him closely and then I recognized him.

"It's Bernard!!" I said with delight.

Here was one of the bosom friends of my boyhood days, whom I had not seen in many years. We stood there talking for five or ten minutes and then, when I heard someone clear his throat a little impatiently, I remembered where I was. Bernard went back to his gardening and I went back to sipping my tea. It didn't seem to me that our hosts were quite as gracious about it as they might have been. It was like I told the children on the way home: "You're always likely to run into an old pal working around somebody's house, aren't you?"

Some days later, Lynn had an invitation to spend the night with a friend who lived on a farm near us. I reminded my daughter about her manners and then I said:

"I'm going to dress you in some dungarees and a clean shirt. You wouldn't want to go to this farm all dressed up and have your friend think you were putting on airs."

She went off barefooted, but when she came back the next day she was wearing a cute little pink dress and a pair of patent-leather shoes.

"Where in the world did you get the clothes?" I asked.

"Betty's mother took us to the movies, so she let me wear some of Betty's things," Lynn said.

"But why did you wear them home?"

"Oh, she said Betty had plenty more dresses and shoes and I could have these, if you weren't too proud to take them. So I remembered you said we shouldn't act stuck up and I told her you weren't the least bit proud."

The high point of the local social season was to be a fair sponsored by the church. All our neighbors would be there, I knew, and it seemed to be a good chance to show how graciously my little family could behave. The children began to prepare for the great event days in advance. There were to be a number of contests and they were getting ready. Larry decided to find an entry for the contest to select the most ferocious-looking garden pest and he captured a large family-size praying mantis with a fierce scowl. Lynn went with me to buy chicken feed one day and picked out a sack with a pretty design. She had the lady next door help her make a dress so she could enter the competition for the prettiest costume made from a feed sack. Janie, who had been tending a couple of pumpkin plants all summer without any notable success, decided to enter her only pumpkin in the contest for the most unusual vegetable. It was about the size of a large apple and perfectly formed. I helped them get their entries ready, and on the day of the big event I dressed everyone in his best clothes and off we went.

"Now, no Katzenjammer stuff," I told them as we were leaving, "we want to make a nice impression."

"They better give me a prize for my bug," Larry said darkly.

"That's not the idea," I said. "Probably, none of you will win prizes. You mustn't act ugly if you don't. You should be good sports when you lose and not want to hog everything."

We looked downright human when we reached the parish hall. I enjoyed the looks of approval which I could see on everyone's face as I walked around with the children. I put myself out to my fullest. I played Truth or Consequences and even smiled happily when I found that my Consequence required that I stand on one leg and eat a piece of watermelon off a table, while my hands were tied behind my back. When the schoolteacher unpacked her banjo and the senior vestryman his mouth organ, I joined in the dancing. I smiled through the Paul Jones, even when I had to give a weight advantage of ten pounds to my partners. Finally the pastor approached me and asked if I wouldn't like to be one of the judges in the contests that were about to come off.

"Maybe I'd better not," I said firmly. "My children have all entered exhibits, you know, and somebody might think I was prejudiced."

"Oh, don't be silly," he said. "Everyone trusts you perfectly."

I tried to get out of it, but there was no way. Be a good sport, I had told the children. So I had to be one myself. Before the judging even started, I knew I would have to vote against all of the entries which the kids had made. But I thought I could find some way to make it up to them later. The two other judges were prominent citizens and I was pleased to have my youngsters see me in such a position of honor and trust.

The first contest was to pick the prettiest dress made from a feed sack. I closed my eyes to Lynn, whose costume was far and away the prettiest. I made up my mind in favor of a stout lady and turned to see what the other judges thought about the situation. They were old buddies and they had their heads together. Finally, one of them turned to me and said:

"We've decided on the little girl there, with the long blonde hair. No question about it, is there?"

I tried to point out the virtues of the stout lady's dress, but I couldn't get anywhere with them. Finally, I explained lamely that the little girl whom they had chosen was my daughter and that I found the situation a little embarrassing.

"Oh, that's all right," they said happily and one of them stood up and called Lynn to the platform to receive the prize.

"What's your name, young lady?" the master of ceremonies asked.

"Lynn Toombs," she said cheerfully.

It took a minute for this one to sink in with the audience, but when they saw my face get red they began to laugh and applaud politely. I heaved a sigh of relief, because it looked as if I had squeaked by all right.

Then we set about judging the most ferocious-looking garden pest. I settled immediately upon a huge green caterpillar, but the other judges were not impressed. It was just a tobacco worm, they assured me, and they had seen hundreds of them and they weren't ferocious at all.

"Now that thing with the long legs there," said one of them, "looks like it's saying its prayers. That's a mean-looking thing."

"Wait a minute," I said frantically. "Look at this spider. He's really ferocious."

"Not as fierce-looking as this praying thing," insisted the other judge. "I think that wins the prize, all right."

My arguments were to no avail, so I shrank down in my seat as they called Larry up to the platform to receive his prize for having the most ferocious-looking insect. When he was called upon to announce his name, I noticed, people didn't laugh very hard. But I got plenty red.

This time, we were to choose the most unusual vegetable. I saw a long green pepper and quickly interested the other judges in its merits. The judges were just about sold on the pepper when one of them picked up Janie's pumpkin. That did it. They both were entranced by the midget-sized vegetable and nothing I could say shook them from their allegiance. Finally, I gave up and began to look around for a place to hide.

Janie was summoned from the audience. She was asked her name, and, with a brevity which I found quite laudable, said:

"Janie."

At least, I muttered, she didn't give her last name. Maybe some people wouldn't recognize her. The master of ceremonies was quite delighted with her and when he picked up the prize that went to the little girl, he got a big laugh from the audience. Because the prize was a heavy stack of crockery, almost as tall as the child herself.

"I bet your mama will be glad to get these," the man said.

"My daddy will," Janie said calmly.

"Well, where's your daddy, then?"

She put her thumb in her mouth and began to look around. Then she saw me and with the index finger of her free hand, she pointed to me.

[201]

" 'Ere's Daddy," she said.

There was an unbelieving gasp as the audience made the connection. The other judges looked at me darkly. The master of ceremonies handed me the dishes and then, to break up the threatening silence which had settled over the hall, he started talking fast.

"Now, we have a little surprise," he said. "This is an unscheduled contest, just to give some of the men a chance at a prize. We want all the men to line up on one side of the hall and you girls on the other. Then, the girls are to pick out the ugliest, meanest-looking man in the place."

In the confusion which followed, I loaded up the children's prizes and we stole out the back door.

I knew who was going to win that last contest and it was just like I had told the children—we didn't want to be hogs about such things.

Chapter Nineteen

IN the course of the months which had passed, I had been forced to master a number of arts and sciences. I had served as a cook, a carpenter, a washer-woman, a painter, a farmer, and, when I had time to work at it, a writer. I had been persuaded that there was no new skill which I could not master. But there was one trade I should never have tackled; I should have left plumbing alone.

I am basically a city boy. To me, water had always been something that came out of the faucet when the handle was turned. Knowing that water fell from the sky and that a large part of the earth's surface was covered with it, I figured it was something like air, or sunshine, that you didn't have to earn, or search for, or worry about. I had always known where my next glass of water was coming from. Until I moved down to the country with the kids, I always knew where my next hot bath was coming from, also.

But the cottage had no running hot water. It had plenty of cold water, which came from a deep artesian well dug thirty years before. My father, who also liked warm showers, had worked out an arrangement for the shower that no one in the world but him could have rigged up. He had put a big pipe up on the roof and run the water line to the shower through this, so that the sun would heat the water. The result was that on hot days, when you yearned for a nice cold shower, you would be hit by a blast of hot water, and on cold, cloudy days, when you wanted a hot shower, you would get ice water. We had survived the winter in Florida without hot water in the house. The children, of course, spent so much time swimming—summer and winter—that I was worried more about barnacles collecting on them than dirt. But now I wanted a hot shower of my own—I was tired of cadging hot baths off the neighbors.

When we returned to Maryland in the spring, I broached to Dad the idea of installing an inexpensive hot-water heater in our cottage. He agreed to shop around in Washington and try to find one. It was about this time that the first, distant rumbling of disaster in our water department could be heard. The artesian well became a little hesitant and there were times when it did not deliver water at all for two or three hours. One day, it quit sending up water entirely, disgorging instead a mixture of mud and black sand. It cost fifty dollars to get the local well digger to clean it out, and then it began to falter again. Whenever I saved up a big stack of dishes to wash, the well would stop. Whenever I brought in kale or turnip greens or some other vegetable which had to be put through seven waters, the system would fail. It was uncanny.

Dad decided that as long as the well was behaving this way, there was no use in buying the hot-water heater. I took the opposite view of the matter, holding that if I wasn't going to be able to take a shower, I would much rather not take a hot shower than not take a cold shower. He couldn't see the logic of this and, come to think of it, I'm not sure that I can either. So I turned my argument in the direction of getting a new well. How could I raise my children properly, I asked him, when I couldn't hold the threat of soap and water over them at all times?

But instead of agreeing to sink another artesian well, Dad came up with a new plan.

"I've got a friend who knows how to dig a shallow well," he confided. "An artesian well will cost us four or five hundred dollars. But we can put down a shallow well for ten or twelve. We can do it ourselves."

"In my spare time?" I asked apprehensively.

"Oh, I'll bring my friend down. He'll do the whole thing."

"Is he a big eater?" I asked.

"Skinny as a rail," Dad assured me.

A couple of weeks later, Dad showed up with the man who was going to do the whole thing. He was skinny all right—he looked as if he hadn't eaten a square meal in five years. This pleased me, since I had to feed him for the week end. But then I started to wonder how any man so frail could be expected to do any work. This really worried me when I saw the equipment that he had brought along for the job—a big post-hole digger, with extensions; a collection of huge wrenches which looked as if they might have been used on the Big Inch pipeline; and a mallet which obviously weighed more than the man himself.

"We may need a little help from you," my father said.

"Yes," I replied, "I'm sure of that."

On Saturday morning, I tried to get the little fellow to eat a big breakfast, on the theory that I might be able to build up his strength a little. But he stuck to orange juice and coffee, so I turned the dishes over to the children for washing and prepared to meet my fate as a well digger.

The first operation was to climb down into the reservoir where we had once stored the overflow from the artesian well. There I found myself surrounded by protesting frogs and faced with the task of knocking a hole through six inches of concrete. The little man who was going to do the whole thing pointed out the star drill to me and Dad volunteered to hold the drill while I wielded a mallet. After a couple of hours of the anvil chorus, I had to excuse myself and climb out of the hole to fix lunch. This pleased the frogs, but Dad was unhappy about the interruption.

After lunch, the little man who was going to do the whole thing gave the post-hole digger half a turn to show me how easy it was. This carried the drill down one inch, and for the next twenty feet I was on my own. We finally reached the point where we had to drive pipe down through solid ground and I found that I was unanimously elected to handle the mallet. I was the only one in the crowd big enough to pick it up. We finally reached water, and when I saw the stuff flow out of the pipe so copiously, I was ready to forgive everyone for everything. When I got back to the house, I kept turning on faucets just to see water run.

When I tried the faucets again the next day, something came out but I wasn't sure it was water. It had a red color. The little man came forward to explain that it was iron in the water.

"You've got to expect that in a shallow well," he said.

"Oh," I said.

Now that we had water, even if it was a little red, I began to yearn mightily for a hot shower again. Dad promised he would buy the heater and so I went on about my business, trying to get used to having water in the house once more. I found that the only clothes that could be washed safely were things which were already red in color. It was not much good for washing dishes, because you couldn't make soapsuds. And it gave you a sort of puckered feeling when you took a shower in it. But I was not one to quibble about such matters. After all, it was wet.

I found out how much I had come to love water when it stopped flowing one day. I investigated and found that the well hadn't gone dry this time. The pump had broken down. This happened just as I was washing the little girls' hair. I had to take them and the shampoo over to the old well to finish the job. After we had rigged up a hand pump on the artesian well we were able to draw a couple of buckets of clear water out of it every day for drinking water. I put the kids' heads under the pump and finished the shampoo there. In the confusion, I went back to the house and left the bottle of shampoo near the pump.

The next day, I sent Lynn and Janie over to draw a bucket of drinking water. They came back a few minutes later to complain that they couldn't get any water from the pump.

"There's a jar of water there," I said. "Pour some of it in the pump to prime it."

Nothing more was heard from them for ten or fifteen minutes and, since I needed the water, I went to see what the trouble was. I found Lynn working the pump handle industriously but nothing was coming out of the well but a stream of bubbles.

"I guess we made a mistake and used the shampoo to prime the pump," she said simply.

I tried the pump for a while, but all I could produce was slightly larger soap bubbles than Lynn had been getting. The whole process delighted Janie and she was chasing the bubbles with loud squeals.

I still couldn't get the pump motor to run and decided I would have to wait until my father arrived that night. I sent the girls over to the mainland for drinking water and Larry helped me carry in several buckets of water which were to be used for flushing the toilet. Dad arrived that night in a happy frame of mind.

"I've got the hot-water heater," he said, first thing.

"Now all we need is the water," I said, giving him a brief fill-in on the situation.

The people next door, who have the misfortune to share the water system with us, had a house full of company that week end. Out of their faucets, on this happy occasion, was coming nothing but a little air and out of the pump was coming nothing but soap-bubbles. So the next morning they urged us to call in a plumber.

"Plumber, nothing," said Dad with determination. "I installed this water system and there's nothing can go wrong with it that I can't fix."

That took care of that—and the rest of the day was spent tearing down the pump and putting it together again. We finally managed to get it working and water flowed out of the faucets —a phenomenon which, by now, I looked upon as little short of miraculous.

"Now can we put in the hot-water heater?" I asked Dad.

"Sure," he said.

We had not progressed much farther than to sort out the collection of second-hand pipe which he had been saving for twenty years for this particular job when Janie came to my side.

"Daddy," she said, a stern look on her face, "I turn on uh water forest, but nuffin comes out."

My father looked at me and I looked at him and without a word we started out to locate the trouble. After we had searched for half an hour, the lady next door appeared and said timidly:

[208]

"The water's off."

"We're working on it," I said amiably enough. "How's the hand pump?"

"Well, you can get some water along with the bubbles, now. It's all right for washing dishes."

"It should be. Pure castile at ninety-eight cents a bottle," I replied sadly.

A few minutes later, Dad and I found the children splashing around happily in a mud puddle which had not been there the day before. This solved the mystery of why we were getting no water in the house—the pipe had broken. The rest of the day was devoted to patching the break with concrete and then we installed our hot-water heater. The following night, Dad said he thought the concrete was hard enough so that we could turn the water on again.

"Think I'll take a hot shower before I go back to town," he said.

Having been sustained for these many weeks by the dream of a hot shower, I sat down to wait my turn. But before Dad had finished, the patched pipe had burst and we were without water—hot or cold—again. The next few days exist as a blur in my memory. I became obsessed with the desire for a hot shower—but every time I got one thing fixed on the water system, something else broke down. We managed to keep the house supplied with salt water from the river, but its uses were limited. We also had some rain water for washing dishes and some well water for drinking. But I was always getting the pails mixed up, flushing the toilet with well water, fixing coffee with rain water, and trying to make ice cubes out of salt water.

Dad and I spent the next week end working on the water system and by Sunday afternoon we were convinced that everything was repaired. We turned on the water and I rushed back to the house to start the hot-water heater—determined that I would, at last, get that shower. I had promised the children a fairly elaborate dish called crab en casserole for dinner that night and, while the water heated, I started to work on it. When the water was hot enough for my shower, I found I was in the midst of getting seven egg whites to stand in peaks. So I called Janie:

"You take a shower, Honey. By the time you're finished, I'll be ready."

But by the time she got out, I was in the midst of mixing dough for toll-house cookies and I sent Lynn in to take a shower. She used all the hot water and now I decided to put off my drenching until after dinner. There was water for dishes and I suggested that Larry take his shower while I was helping the girls with the drying. It takes fifty gallons of water when Larry takes a shower and therefore, before he was finished, the tank was empty again.

By now, I had three clean and shining youngsters and I decided to put them to bed before they could become otherwise. I sat down in an easy chair to wait for the water to heat up once more. Somehow, I dozed off and, an hour later, awoke in a panic. I rushed to the shower room and turned the hot-water handle. There was a gurgle and three drops of luke-warm water came out. I was dirty, I was tired, and I was as frustrated as man can get. In a dark mood, I set out to repair the system. I discovered that the concrete patch had crumbled, allowing all the hot water to leak out of the system. By this time, I was ready to settle for even a cold shower, and so I tried to make a temporary repair. Working in the dark, it took a long time, and when I finally threw the switch to start the motor, nothing happened. I didn't even take the trouble to find out what was the matter. I walked back to the house twice as dirty, twice as tired, and twice as frustrated as when I had started.

I took a look at the clock and shrugged. It wouldn't have made much difference, anyway. It was past midnight now and much too late to be taking a shower.

Chapter Twenty

THE trouble with children, I finally decided, is that they are completely illogical. This hardly startling discovery came to me one day when things had progressed in a particularly mad way. Lynn and Janie had been making a complete dinner for the fifteen Tweenies and Foo Young—out of some black mud they had found in the creek. Larry was entertaining a boy his own age. In the end, of course, the boys had found it compulsory to smear the girls with mud. I brought the girls in to clean them up and sent the boys out to the river to swim. Janie had finished her shower and came out into the living room, dripping water all over the place.

"Dry yourself, sister," I said.

"But, Daddy, I can't," she replied.

"Why not?" I asked wearily.

"Can't find my towel."

"Well, look for it."

She thought about this for a brief moment, then said:

"But Daddy, how can I find it when I don't eben know where tuh look?"

"All right," I said wearily, "use Lynn's then."

When the girls had dressed, I sent them out to play. Larry came into the house and within a few minutes was displaying the same talent for making no sense.

"Listen to those silly girls," he said to me. "Hear them out there playing momma and papa?"

"Uh huh," I replied.

"Girls are so silly," he continued. "Whenever a couple of girls get together, that's all they do is play some silly game like that."

"Terrible, isn't it?"

"Yeah, Peter and I had something intelligent to talk about. Not that silly stuff."

"What were you talking about?" I asked.

"Girls," he said, quite seriously.

All of this made some sort of impression upon me, because I had been brooding over the complete failure of all the systems I had tried for handling the children. In the time I had been taking care of them, they had carried out a successful revolt against a military dictatorship, had run a free-enterprise economy into quick bankruptcy, and had put such a strain upon a democratic system of life that I had been forced to abandon it.

No wonder, I thought, I can't fit these children into any logical system of behavior—they are completely illogical. They can't understand discipline, either in light or heavy syrup, and they don't understand rewards. There is no system by which you can raise children, I concluded. A parent who believes that there is, I went on unhappily, is just like a horse player who thinks he's got a system to beat the races—both of them die broke.

It was later that day when I ran across an article describing the functioning of an English school where the progressive system of education was being used. In this school, the children were allowed to do just what they wanted to—whether it was

[213]

breaking up the furniture or telling lies. The main objective was to keep them from developing inhibitions. In my mood of that day, this struck me as a reasonable approach to the problem. If systems didn't work, why not try no system? It sounded easy, anyway, so I decided just to let the children do as they pleased and stop worrying about it.

Within a few days, I had lost any illusions about this way of life being easy. It's easy on the children, but it requires a lot of the parent. I found myself picking up an endless stream of clothes and toys and yielding to a never-ceasing stream of whims. I discovered that when conditions of life did not suit the children entirely, they would turn on me with long and bitter tirades. But I couldn't correct them when they got snippy—for each tirade against me, I was led to understand, represented one less inhibition that might develop.

My father took a very dim view of this whole experiment. Being a proper gentleman, he suffered most acutely when the children were being Progressive at mealtime. With some sort of philosophical detachment, I had grown accustomed to dodging the biscuits which they passed by air mail and I had learned to look both ways before taking a piece of fried chicken off the platter so as to avoid being speared. But Dad wore a martyred expression through every meal, now, and one morning the long overdue explosion occurred.

It was at breakfast, and I was in the kitchen cooking pancakes when I heard his voice raised in anger. Larry came racing out into the kitchen a moment later. He had spilled the milk, he told me, while having a race with the girls to see who could slide a box of cereal across the table fastest. His grandfather had sent him out to the kitchen to get a rag to clean up the mess.

[214]

"Grumpy Grampa's really on a rampage this morning," he said happily.

In days gone by, such a slighting reference to my father would have brought down my wrath upon Larry. But, being quite progressive now, I merely shrugged it off. I cooked a stack of pancakes, took them to the table, and set them down between Larry and Dad. Larry dived in immediately and started to pick the ones he wanted. The one on top was a little too brown for him, so he picked up the next one for inspection. Dad was glowering at this.

"Help yourself to some cakes, Dad," I suggested.

"I'm waiting for Larry to pick out the ones he wants," Dad snapped. "I'll see what's left."

I ducked out on this battle and went back to cook some more. When I came back with the second stack, I found Dad sitting at the table, his arms crossed and his forehead wrinkled into a dark scowl. He had not eaten any of the pancakes.

"What's the trouble?" I asked. "Why don't you eat some pancakes?"

"Larry's been shuffling these and dealing them out like a pack of cards," he said. "I don't think his hands are any too clean."

I gave Dad the fresh cakes and went off to ponder the situation. If the children weren't developing inhibitions, I knew I was getting a few.

The following week end, my young sister, home from her travels for a time, came down with Dad. She explained that Dad's reports of life in our house, now that everyone had complete freedom, had so intrigued her that she wanted to see for herself. As things worked out, she got the full treatment.

This got under way the following evening when we were

paid a visit by an old friend of the family. She was a gray spinster lady whose ideas of the proprieties might be conservatively described as rigid. She had known me since I was in knee pants, but she would never come to our house unless properly chaperoned by some female member of my family. Since my sister was present tonight, she had come to call. The children gave her a small taste of progressivism before I got the girls to bed. I handed Larry a copy of one of the popular scientific magazines in the hope that it would keep him quiet long enough for Dad to carry on a conversation with the lady.

The boy was curled up under the lamp, engrossed in what he was reading. I was quite relieved, because the lady was of the children-should-be-seen school and mine had already made themselves heard too much that evening. But when I looked a little more closely at what Larry was reading, I began to feel some anxiety. The article which held his attention so closely was headed: "The Birth of a Baby—With Sixteen Color Photos."

Dad and the spinster lady were skipping about lightly on such subjects of conversation as geranium culture, crocheting, and the use of herbs in cooking. I listened politely, but all the time I was watching that kid out of the corner of my eye. Finally, there came a brief lull in the adult conversation while Dad tried to recall what *filé* was extracted from. I heard Larry say:

"Daddy."

"Yes," I said quietly.

"What's the u-m-b-i-l-i-c-a-l cord?"

Dad cleared his throat nervously. The spinster fluttered her handkerchief anxiously. My sister stifled something that had all the earmarks of a loud guffaw. But, being a progressive parent, I didn't bat an eyelash and gave Larry the best concise explanation possible under the circumstances. By the tone of

[216]

my voice, I tried to convey to him the thought that conversation on the subject was closed. He listened closely and said nothing for a moment. That little breathing space was all Dad needed to get the conversation back to the subject of sweet marjoram. But Larry was just thinking out his next question. Then he asked:

"Daddy, in the days before they had doctors, how did they know how to cut this cord?"

"They just knew, I guess."

"But suppose they didn't know—what happened?"

"I don't know," I said.

Grandfather was obviously quite anxious to get this over with, because he stepped in with a considered explanation of how people knew and what happened. I was relieved to see that Larry was satisfied by this and he went back to a study of the magazine. The spinster expelled the breath that she had been holding for so long.

Dad was determined to keep control of the conversation from here on out. He launched immediately into a description of the beauties of the sunset that evening. His theory was, apparently, that if he could talk long enough, Larry would forget the next question, whatever it might be. Dad was describing the burnt-senna effect of the sunset and the way it had been reflected on the water when Larry, oblivious to what was being said, piped up again:

"Daddy."

"Be quiet," I whispered. "You're interrupting."

I realized that this was unprogressive and I immediately began to hate myself for having halted the little fellow's questionings.

But Dad looked happy and he was carrying the ball for all

[217]

he was worth. He was now describing every contour of a tiny pink cloud which had floated high in the green sky after the sun had disappeared. Without pausing for breath, he began to describe the scene in reverse—telling how the cloud looked as reflected in the still water.

I was watching the boy out of the corner of my eye. He was sitting there with his mouth open, his eyes glued on his grandfather. He was not, I knew, listening to a word that was being spoken. He was just waiting for his grandfather to stop talking for one instant so he could get in his next question. Dad talked until his face began to get purple. He understood Larry's purpose also, and he was determined to talk him down. But Dad ran out of breath at last and Larry pounced like a cat.

"Daddy," he said.

"Now, son . . ." I admonished.

"Well, gee whizz, when do I get a chance to talk?" he demanded petulantly.

"For heaven's sake," Dad growled. "What is it this time, Larry?"

I saw the handkerchief flutter quickly in the lady's hand.

"There's a word here I can't pronounce," said Larry. "It's spelled this way—a-n-e-s-t-h-e-t-h-e. . . ."

"Oh, that's *anesthetic*," I said hurriedly and then tried to throw a quick pass to my father, "did you notice the color of the water in close to shore, Dad?"

"No, that's not it," said Larry, completely wrecking my attempt to get the play back on the center of the field. "It's not *anesthetic*. I know that word. This is a-n-e-s-t-h-e-s-i-a. It says that sometimes the mother comes out of this before the baby is even wrapped in a blanket."

"Oh," I said, "that word's *anesthesia*."

[218]

"What in the world is that boy reading?" Dad asked.

"What's it for?" Larry asked.

"Women find childbirth painful. They give them an anesthetic, just like for an operation," I said. "Dulls the pain somewhat."

"Oh," he said.

He went back to his reading and my sister gave way to a violent fit of coughing. The spinster, whose face was as white as her handkerchief, had now opened her purse. She was taking off her glasses and putting them away. The handkerchief followed and she shut the purse with a hard snap and gave it an angry pat. She uncrossed her ankles and I knew she was getting out of there while the getting was good. She looked a little dazed and was wearing a fixed, painful sort of smile, as if she had just come out of the monkey house at the zoo on a warm spring day. She didn't move hurriedly and I could only assume that it was because she felt a little faint. Whatever cause slowed her down, it gave Larry the time he needed.

"Daddy, what is the p-l-a-c-e-n . . ."

I had my mouth open and was just waiting for him to finish spelling the word. But Dad didn't wait that long.

"I think," Grandfather said sternly, "that for a little boy his age, umbilical cord is about as far as you need to go."

The lady was on her feet now and it was obvious that she had no desire to stick around and see how this came out. We walked to the door with her and I heaved a mighty sigh of relief as she walked down the path. When I got back in the living room, Larry was waiting for me, magazine in hand.

"What is that, Daddy? P-l-a-c—"

"I'd have to look that one up myself, Sonny," I said. "I just wouldn't . . ."

[219]

"Oh, I'll explain it to him," my sister said impatiently.

Larry listened to her thoughtfully. When she had finished, he turned to me and said with admiration:

"A woman would know a thing like that, wouldn't she?"

I spent the rest of the evening in the living room alone, staring into the fireplace. The progressive system of raising children was the subject uppermost in my mind. I studied it from all angles. Then I went to bed.

The next morning, before I had been able to brew coffee, Larry came racing through the kitchen and knocked over a can of fruit juice that I had just opened. He continued on his merry way, in the fashion which had become usual under the new system.

"Hey," I yelled. "Don't you even say you're sorry?"

"Aw, your grandmother's whiskers," my progressive prodigy replied, "you oughtn't to leave stuff around like that."

I reached for my long-handled pancake turner with one hand and, as he came back through the kitchen, I grabbed him with the other hand.

"Bend over," I ordered.

Then I applied the pancake turner, in a most unprogressive manner, where I thought it would do the most good.

Chapter Twenty-one

Every summer house comes equipped with week-end guests. They come as surely as the sunshine, the gentle rains, the flowers, and the bluebirds. They brighten, or darken, the host's life for a couple of days and then depart, leaving in their wake a stack of dirty dishes, the remnants of whatever gift of candy or potables they came bearing, and an odd assortment of single stockings, bathing-suit tops, and keys to houses in town. The loss of the latter is never discovered until the guests are well on their way and imposes upon the host the necessity of making a rush trip to the post office on Monday to catch the first outgoing mail.

It is idle to speculate about the question of whether week-end company is worth the trouble. I found that it added a certain piquancy and flavor to a life which was not entirely devoid of either. I have never had guests whom I wouldn't want to have again, but I am not sure that my guests have always felt the same way about it, for it took a rugged character to survive a week end at our place.

Our main week ender, of course, was my father. He could hardly qualify as a guest, but was more like one of the permanent fixtures. Dad viewed the whole proceedings with misgivings, and his week-end visits were undertaken with the sort of spirit in which a missionary goes forth to make a call on a tribe of headhunters. He came every week, determined to set us aright, and went back a bitter, defeated man. The other members of my family—my mother and my sister—did not come so regularly. I suppose this was because it took them so long to rest up between visits. For, the minute either of them walked into the place, they saw things that had to be done. The girls would get shampooed, the closets would be cleaned, or the curtains would be washed. Mother almost always left some small monument to her visit, such as a jar of cookies or a lemon meringue pie.

As for my friends, I can say that I always warned them what they were getting into. I told them that the house and its parts —faucets, electric switches, doors and windows—were subject to change without notice. I warned them that the place was populated by small fiends, who wouldn't think of sleeping past six-thirty in the morning, who left fishhooks hanging in the dark corners of closets and who kept snapping turtles in the wash basins. I told them about Tonker who liked nothing better, after a frolic in the black swamp mud, than to curl up in someone's open suitcase for a nap. I told them about the cats, who specialized in playing tug-o-war with nylon stockings. After I had told them all these things, I felt that they were forewarned and I refused to accept responsibility. Once they reached the premises, I did not expect them to do much but defend themselves.

There were some skeptics who did not believe that life could possibly be as wild and woolly as I pictured it. Among these were two of my closest friends, a married couple, who decided that they would come and see for themselves. They were due to arrive one Friday. This was at the time when the water system was doing its best to drive me back to civilization. It broke down in three or four places the day before my friends were to arrive, and I telephoned to my father and suggested that he get in touch with the friends and postpone their visit. I spent the next day in a vain effort to restore the water system and didn't even have a chance to give the house its normal pre-week-end cleaning. When Dad arrived, I went out to the car to meet him and there, of course, I found my friends, smiling happily.

"We decided to come anyway," they said. "Things can't be as bad around here as you say."

"But the water . . ." I started to say.

"There's plenty of water in the river for us," one of them said cheerfully.

This was one of those great truths which I love so much. My only problem, then, was to get the water from the river to the house. This I did by hand, filling numerous buckets, cooking utensils, and dishpans with salt water for use in the bathroom. I went to sleep that night in a considerable state of exhaustion. But I was not so tired that I could sleep through the noise that followed. The first time I was awakened was when the lady guest, groping toward the bathroom in a strange house, wound up instead in a washtub full of salt water. She had wedged herself in, so that it was necessary for me to assist her husband in getting her out. An hour after we had restored order, Dad got up and put his foot in a dishpan full of water and his fervent curses awakened me again.

It was almost dawn when Tonker started to chase the cats around the house. One cat and Tonker fell in the fresh-water bucket and the ruckus which resulted from this awakened everyone. After all this, I hoped to be able to sleep late, but I woke up to find Father standing by my bed.

"Are you going to sleep all day?" he asked, and I could see that he was quite annoyed.

"Groomph," I said sleepily.

"Your company's up and dressed and waiting for breakfast. My goodness."

"What time is it?" I asked, trying to get really awake.

"It's a quarter past seven," he said. "I should think you'd learn to get up around here."

My guests were waiting in the living room. The happy shouts of children at play had awakened them. When I walked into the living room they were watching with amusement as the children sailed toy boats across the floor. Whatever water had not been spilled by adults and animals during the night, the children had sloshed about in the morning. Now they were making bets on which of their boats would sail out the front door first.

At the beginning of the visiting season this summer I was a little apprehensive about the whole thing, but as the weeks went by and my friends still spoke to me after weekending chez Toombs, I began to feel a little easier about the prospects.

It was well toward the end of the summer when the week end came along which threatened to end all week ends—everywhere. I had a friend from Army days who was a psychiatrist and I asked him to come down to visit us. He accepted, and I began early in the week to try to get the children in the habit of acting Normal.

I didn't get very far because on Wednesday we found we were going to have more company than we had bargained for—

[224]

another friend who is an artist and who specializes in work with animals. Since we had more animals around our place than could be found anywhere outside of a zoo, he often dropped by to spend a couple of days doing sketches of our dogs, cats, frogs, turtles, fish, or chickens. This Wednesday, he showed up unexpectedly and said he planned to stay down over the week end. He unloaded his suitcase and then pulled out of the car a wooden carrying case which was giving off an ominous thumping sound.

"What's this?" I asked.

"That," he said happily, "is Philip, the rabbit."

"Noisy, isn't he?"

"Not as long as he's traveling. He just starts to kick the cage when I stop moving."

He went on to explain that Philip was a Giant Checker, whom he had rented as a model. He was quite a rabbit, nearly two feet long and beautifully marked. My friend resisted my suggestion that Philip spend his time in the coop with the chickens and insisted that the rabbit would be happy only in the house.

"Is he, er, that is, does he know how to behave himself in the house?" I asked.

"Oh, he's housebroken," my friend assured me. "Just spread out some newspapers for him in a corner."

I shrugged and let it go at that. In my young life, one rabbit named Philip was not going to make any difference. Worse things than that happened to me every day. So I went ahead, trying to get the children ready for presentation to the psychiatrist and not paying too much attention to Philip's antics.

When the psychiatrist arrived, the children were sitting on the front porch, watching the rabbit hop around. It was quite a pretty picture and the children all came forward pleasantly to meet the doctor. But Philip sat there glowering and I had a fleeting idea that he had taken a dislike to the psychiatrist.

Actually, until this time, Philip had been a fairly pleasant house guest. His single weakness lay in the fact that he was likely to mistake any newspaper which might be lying around the house for the piece of newspaper he was supposed to use. When the new guest arrived, Philip lost the spotlight which he had been occupying, and I suppose this made him unhappy.

He took it out on the cats, chasing them around the living room. The cats, dismayed by the rabbit's sudden charges, climbed up people's backs, knocked over flower pots, and committed other acts of violence. Tonker decided to get into the act at this point and he began to chase Philip. Then Philip turned around and began to chase Tonker. Within a few minutes, the living room was a shambles. Books were knocked over, drinks spilled, chairs upset, and almost everyone was bearing the scars of battle. The children were screaming happily. Never in their wildest dreams had they been able to conjure up a picture of such joyous destruction as this. They began to chase the animals and, occasionally, one of the animals would stop running and chase a child.

"Perhaps," I suggested to the artist, "we'd better put Philip back in his cage."

But within a few minutes, the rabbit was pounding so hard that we decided to give him the freedom of one of the bedrooms. Every now and then some child would let him out, but in spite of this I tried to get the week end back on a nice, social basis. For the psychiatrist's benefit, I was attempting to create the illusion that my house was as well managed as other mental institutions.

[226]

When Larry short-sheeted the doctor's bed on Friday night, I let it go with a patient shrug. Nor did I lose my temper when I found that the pungent odor in the living room emanated from the remains of a mouse that had passed away, unnoticed, in Lynn's hospital for injured animals. But the calm I had affected for the psychiatrist was shattered when I was cooking dinner on Saturday night. I had gathered vegetables from the garden to make a salad, and while I was talking to my guests on the front porch, the salad ingredients disappeared. I suspected the children but, since they weren't around, I couldn't prove anything. So I picked more vegetables, made the salad, and went back to visit with my company.

Some fifteen minutes later, I found the salad missing again. It occurred to me that the children, no salad lovers, had been playing a Katzenjammer trick and, angrily, I called them on the carpet.

"We didn't do it," said Lynn. "Maybe it was Tonker."

"More likely your cats," Larry said indignantly.

"Tonker and the cats don't eat salad," I said sternly.

"Maybe," suggested Janie, "it was 'at rarebit did it."

"No rabbit could eat that much," I said sharply.

At this moment, I became aware that the psychiatrist was standing in the door, watching me scold the children.

"They do things around here," I told him, after I had sent them on their way, "and just won't admit them."

"Well," he said, in gentle reproof, "you have to be careful not to accuse children of something they didn't do."

In spite of the fact that Philip kept breaking loose, we had a peaceful dinner and a quiet evening. I tried to steer the conversation around to the point where I could get my psychiatrist friend's opinion of the children, but he was bent on getting to bed early. He said good night, but had been in his room only a few minutes when he returned to the group, grinning a little sheepishly.

"I guess you were right about the children," he said. "Last night they short-sheeted my bed—and tonight, this."

He held out a double armload of vegetables.

"Where did you find those?" the artist asked suddenly.

"In my bed," said the doctor.

I groaned—but not as loudly as the artist.

"Kids, nothin," the artist said. "That's one of Philip's tricks. Hides that stuff in bed and eats it later. Terrible mess."

The next afternoon, the children and the artist went off to hunt for crabs. Dad went up on the roof with a bucket of tar. I sat down on the porch with the doctor, hopeful that now at long last I might be able to get him to tell me whether my children would really grow up to be People. We had not been talking long when Dad finished on the roof. Instead of coming in through a door, he climbed in the window of the room where Philip was incarcerated. Coming into the living room, Dad left the door open behind him and Philip hopped out, scowling ominously. Later, I realized why he was angry. I had forgotten to put any newspaper down for him. Now, as he emerged, there was one thought uppermost in his mind. He took a look around the living room and the only piece of paper he could see was one which was resting on the psychiatrist's lap.

Before I could fully appraise the situation, Philip hopped toward the doctor and leaped on to the paper.

"Oh," I said, suddenly divining the beast's purpose, "you'd better put him down—"

But it was too late. The psychiatrist grabbed Philip and tried to get rid of him. But Philip had no intention of being separated

[228]

from a paper at a moment like this. So he sank his teeth into the doctor's hand in a very determined fashion. As I rushed to the rescue, Philip turned on me. I took refuge on the seat of the chair and Philip sat on the floor just waiting for me to come down and fight. The children burst in just then to find me on the buffet and the doctor in very poor shape, indeed.

"Look out," I yelled, "this rabbit's on a rampage."

Lynn either didn't hear me or didn't pay any attention. She walked right over to the ferocious Philip and picked him up.

"You naughty boy," she said. "What are you doing out?"

The scowl left Philip's face immediately, and he went along quietly.

We bandaged up the psychiatrist and he decided that he had better leave before supper. As the guests were packing, someone let Philip loose again and he seemed to be hopping toward the psychiatrist. The doctor grabbed a broom and took up a defensive position.

"One more step," he said grimly, "and I'll knock you right through the ceiling, so help me."

Philip crouched there, scowling and twitching his upper lip nervously so as to show his teeth. The psychiatrist looked just as fierce, as he tried to stare the rabbit down. After a moment I noticed that *his* lip was twitching, too. The artist interceded and put Philip in his box and Philip started to kick. Just then Dad came in and said:

"The tide's up over the road. We won't be able to leave for a while."

Everyone sat down again. All except Philip, who was beating a steady tattoo on his box.

"I better let him out," said the artist. "He'll drive us nuts."

From the look the psychiatrist gave him, I deduced that, according to best available medical opinion, this was not so much a danger as an accomplished fact. Turned loose, Philip looked around for a moment and then hopped determinedly into the room where the doctor had been sleeping.

"Probably looking for that salad stuff he hid last night," the artist said.

After a time, everyone went outside but the doctor. Then, I decided to make a final effort to have a heart-to-heart talk with him.

"What do you really think of this outfit?" I asked timidly.

"Well . . ." he said, and smiled.

I waited, holding my breath, for him to say something more. But he just sat there, looking thoughtful. I began to fidget.

"It's hard to know what to do with children," I said hopefully.

"Yes, it is," he said.

I began to squirm, interpreting his noncommital silence as the worst sort of condemnation. He continued to look thoughtful and I tactfully changed the subject. At last, Dad came back to announce that the tide had gone down enough to make the road passable.

"I'd better get Philip," said the artist.

He and Lynn went off to look for ferocious Philip and I decided to try for *some* reassuring word from my friend.

"Do you think the children will grow up all right, this way?" I asked. "Could you make any suggestions?"

He gave me a sweet, sad smile.

"Oh, don't worry," he said quietly. "I'm sure they'll grow up."

"But . . ." I started to plead.

"I'd better close up my suitcase," he said. "Don't want to keep your father waiting."

He was back a minute later, looking grim.

[230]

"Are they still looking for that rabbit?" he asked.

"Yes," said the artist. "Is he in there?"

"I am no veterinarian," said the doctor, "but I can tell you that rabbit is no gentleman."

The artist laughed nervously and asked:

"What's he done, now?"

"*She*," said the psychiatrist, "crawled up into my suitcase and gave birth to some little rabbits."

The artist looked dumbfounded. Then he laughed.

"Well, at least she knew who the doctor in the crowd was," he said. "What should we do?"

"I am not a doctor to rabbits," my friend said, "especially *that* rabbit. There is nothing in my oath that covers her."

"What'll I do?" wailed the artist. "I've just got a little apartment. I can't take all those rabbits back there."

"You can't leave them here," I roared. "*No one* would be safe."

"Oh, Daddy, Daddy, let us keep them," Lynn pleaded.

"I wanna bunny rarebit," wailed Janie.

This was too much for me. I turned on them fiercely and yelled:

"Shut up and get out of here, the whole bunch of you kids."

I looked at the psychiatrist and saw him, for the first time, nodding approval. Then I turned to the artist.

"Look pal, those rabbits all came in that little box, and so help me, they're all going back in it."

They did. And that was the last time I ever had a rabbit down for the week end.

Chapter Twenty-two

O UR clock stopped one day during the summer. When I tried to get the time from the radio, I found that the static was so heavy it drowned out local stations. During the evening, I could get nothing closer than Des Moines, Fort Worth, or New Orleans. Since I could never understand the relation of Eastern Daylight to Central Standard, I went to bed that night without knowing what time it was. By the next day, I had lost interest in the whole subject. I fixed meals when we got hungry and we went to bed when we got tired.

To the natives around our creek, clocks are something they have heard rumors about, but never use. To whatever extent they measure time, it is by the position of the sun. There is sun-up, a while after sun-up, and then the sun's high in the sky. After that, the sun is lowering, the sun is low, and the sun is down. They go to bed at sun-down, then it's night—and who cares what time it is?

Liberated from enslavement by the timepiece, we had freedom to savor the life we were leading. I liked to watch the children race across the road from the mainland, dressed in whatever odds and ends of clothes they had found that morning, shouting "pow, pow" as they played cowboys and Indians. I would stop whatever I might be doing and smile happily when I saw them run out of the front door and splash their little brown bodies into the water. They had freedom here and were living in the atmosphere that was meant for young things.

It got so I had a little freedom myself—time to watch the sun go down and the moon come up; to follow the beaten silver path along the river as the sun moved from east to west; to stop a little while at twilight to gaze across the creek, where I could see, above a wisp of mist rising from the water, the orange light of a kerosene lantern in a cabin window. We liked the country.

When school started, of course, we had to set the clock again. But I kept as far from it as possible. The calendar was something I managed to keep my distance from, also. But one day, I found a broken pane of glass in the chicken house and looked about for something to stuff in the hole. Then I came across a calendar given us by some storekeeper. After studying it, I reckoned that it was now mid-October. I had been looking after the children for some fourteen months.

It was about this time that I received a letter from my traveling sister. She had managed, while visiting an isolated Caribbean island, of course, to rent a New York apartment. The place was big enough for all of us, she said. I read the children part of her letter:

It seems to me, brother mine, that you and your brood have been gypsies long enough. If I could take the housekeeping over for you, perhaps you could all get "respectable" again. I'd like to see what you look like with a shave and a business suit and a shirt and necktie. Since you came back from the wars, you've just been writing when you needed eating money. Maybe now's the time to get back to a regular job and go after the big money.

Here I paused to look at the children and found they were listening closely, but their expressions reflected puzzlement. I read on:

I know of a nice French school the girls can enter and this will give them a chance to wear some of those pretty little dresses that have been on the hangers for so long. We won't be too far from a park—sandboxes, and roller skating, and things like that after school.

All of this, I tried to make sound exciting, and I glanced at the girls to determine their reaction. All I could see were two lower lips stuck out, and I went on quickly:

We'll find a nice boy's school for Larry—perhaps he would like to board and come home for week ends. He'll need shoes and suits and shirts to replace the things he's outgrown. There are plenty of things for a boy to do in the city—the children's theater, art classes, and I heard about a swimming club with an indoor pool.

It should be great fun for all of us and it will give me a chance to really learn how to cook for a big family. I won't promise to fix all the goofy things you cook, but I'll do my best.

I'll be in New York in a couple of weeks to look the place over, and then I'll let you know the situation.

The children were somewhat less than overjoyed at the prospect. But I did all I could to convince them that a change like this would be best for us. And I kept telling myself that it would be nice, too—no more housework, no more drudgery. But some-

[235]

how, I couldn't picture myself reduced again to the status of a mere father.

The more I thought about it, the more sentimental I seemed to grow. I dwelt with nostalgia upon the times we had known together. This mood held me for a few days and I wandered about with the sweet, patient mien of a saint. I didn't scold the girls when their hair was full of sand—because I would wonder, as I washed it out, what life would be like when my sister took over the job. When Larry decided in the morning, after I had used up all the pancake batter, that he wanted more breakfast, I would mix up another batch without a murmur. Then I would remind myself that the number of pancakes I'd cook for my little family in the future was strictly limited.

But I guess my head isn't quite the right shape for a halo. The one I was trying on for size began to slip very quickly. Tonker got playful and chewed up two of my record albums. The cats stole the fish I was going to have for dinner. Janie broke two of my best glasses in the course of a tea party for Foo Young and the fifteen Tweenies. I heard the school bus driver was threatening to quit his job if Larry and Lynn didn't learn to behave. So I began to employ some harsh words on the whole bunch of them.

Then a northeast wind brought cold and rain. This went on for days, and it wasn't long before we used up the firewood and I found myself dashing out in the wind and rain to chop more. There were no pretty sunsets, and all that was left to remind us of the joys of summer were a few birds. They sat in a row on the telephone wires, facing into the cold, wet wind, and after a few days of it they headed south. It was while chopping wood that I dropped the axe on my foot, damaging a big toe. Then I caught my finger in the pump belt and lost most

[236]

of a fingernail. These mishaps meant that I couldn't walk around very well and couldn't use the typewriter at all. That left me with nothing to do but think. Somehow, life in the country wasn't looking so good just then and I found myself anticipating with eagerness now life in a New York apartment, with my sister to take care of the children.

One night, Lynn came home from school with a rash on her face. The next morning, it had spread considerably. This looked like a case for the doctor and that raised a new question. In all the time we had been in Maryland, we had never been sick enough to need a doctor. I knew there was one around the neighborhood somewhere, and so I set off to the store to telephone for him. The operator finally located the doctor at the home of a woman who was busy having a baby. He said he'd come when he could.

I rather expected to see him arrive on mule back, but a couple of hours later an automobile pulled into the yard. Rushing to the yard I asked:

"Are you the doctor?"

"Yes, sir, Cap'n. I'm what's left of him."

He reminded me immediately of Saint Nick, with his round little belly that shook like a bowl full of jelly. His pants were supported by a belt, and it looked as if it was going to slip any minute either up or down off the high point. His suit was wilted, his collar was a little dirty, his felt hat was tattered, and his black, high-top shoes were muddy.

"My little girl's all broken out with a rash," I said breathlessly, as he dragged a couple of black handbags out of the car.

He stood looking at the surroundings, sniffing the breeze, and contemplating the willow tree in the yard.

"Haven't been down here for twenty years," he said thoughtfully. "Nope, must have been thirty, maybe thirty-five years."

"She's in the house," I reminded him anxiously.

"Had to come over in a boat in the old days," he went on, still looking around the place. "Never knew you'd put a road into here, Cap'n."

"This way, Doctor," I said frantically.

He started with me toward the house. When we got to the front steps, he stopped to look around again.

"Been practicing medicine fifty years," he said. "Fifty years come November, boss."

"Really?" I said. "She's right in here, Doctor."

"How old do you think I am, Cap'n?" he asked, planting himself firmly in my path.

"Well, I would guess about sixty," I said. "But you must be more than that."

"Seventy-six years old," he said triumphantly. "Seventy-six years old. Too old for this sort of thing, boss. Too old."

Suddenly, he remembered what he had come for and walked into the house. Lynn raised her head feebly and cocked an eye at the doctor.

"Hello, Honey," he said. "Where'd you get that head of pretty blonde hair?"

"It itches," said Lynn, pointing to her rash.

"How old do you think this old doctor man is, Honey?"

"Owoooh!" she replied.

"Can I get anything for you?" I asked hastily.

"Just bring me a glass of spring water, if you please, suh," he said.

I did and he drank it.

"Now, would you put some water on to boil?" he asked. "And bring me another glass of spring water, Cap'n. Want to wash off

[238]

my thermometer and take this pretty little girl's temperature."

"What do you think she's got, Doctor?"

"Been up all night, Cap'n," he said, sticking the thermometer in Lynn's mouth and grasping her wrist to take her pulse. "Man my age shouldn't be doing this. Thought I was getting to bed early night before last, but when I looked at the clock it was five-thirty in the morning, Cap'n. And I was up again at seven. Pulse's normal. Now let's see if you've got a temperature, Honey."

"Did you look at her face, yet?" I asked.

"No temperature," he said.

Now he was looking at her throat. There wasn't much bulk to the child, and I knew that he'd have to look at the rash sooner or later. He couldn't miss it.

"It's not poison ivy, I know," I said. "It's something worse."

"Nothing wrong with her throat. That water boiling yet, Cap'n?"

I went to get the water and when I came back he was listening to her chest. Then he had her say "Ah" a couple of times.

"What's your name, Honey?" he asked.

"Lynn," she said.

"Liz? That's a pretty name."

Now he was looking in her eyes with a flashlight. I could stand it no longer.

"That rash, Doctor," I said, raising my voice a little. "What's the rash?"

"Oh, that," he said casually, training his flashlight on her head and looking at her scalp carefully. "Why, Cap'n, that's impetigo. Knew it the minute I walked in the door."

"Impetigo!" I cried in dismay. "Where in the world could she get that?"

"At school, Cap'n, from some child. About this time of year,

[239]

a lot of folks quit taking baths until the weather gets warm again. Not like you and me, Cap'n. There's lots of impetigo around in the winter. Head lice, too. But this little girl hasn't caught any of those, yet."

"Lice?" I said, unbelieving.

"Yes, sir, Cap'n. Nothing to be ashamed of, you know. These children catch them from the dirty children at school."

By now he was rummaging through one of his suitcases. I glanced in it and saw that he was packing around everything that a city drugstore carries, except the soda fountain, cigar stand, and cosmetics counter. I was fascinated at the rows and rows of little bottles and looked more closely. There was a bottle of pink pills, labeled "Aspirin." Next to it was a bottle of blue pills, labeled "Aspirin." By the time I had stopped gawking, I had counted aspirin in six shades and had come to bella donna.

"Don't need drugstores here in the country, boss," he said. "And it's a good thing, because we don't have 'em."

He was making up a couple of envelopes full of pills, including one of green aspirin, and was filling a jar with some salve. By now Lynn was so fascinated she had forgotten that she was itching. She was listening with rapt attention while the doctor told me when and how to use the medicine. Then he started to pack up his bags.

"Afraid you'll have to be pretty careful with her, boss. Probably be in bed a week or ten days. You'll have to change her clothes twice a day and give her clean sheets every day. Boil out everything you take off her, Cap'n, or it'll just keep spreading."

I groaned and he started to leave.

"You'll send me a bill, doctor?"

"Yes sir, boss. I better write it down."

[240]

He rummaged around and found a wrapping off an old bandage. He scribbled my name on it and stuffed it in his pocket.

"Going to get those bills out, one of these weeks now," he said. "Going to get some sleep, too. Been practicing fifty years now and haven't had a good night's sleep for fifty-one. Getting too old, boss. Yes sir, too old."

When he had left, Lynn looked at me wonderingly.

"Gee, country doctors are different, aren't they?" she said.

"Lots of things are different in the country," I said, as I started to strip the sheets off her bed. "Better take off those things, Honey. I can see I've got a lot of boiling to do."

The next three days were spent in a cloud of steam. I think I did nothing but boil clothes and bedding. The rain continued and nothing on the line ever got dry. Every time I itched, I hurried to the mirror to see whether I was breaking out too. Larry was going to school every day now and, though I am a firm believer in education, I began to wonder whether it was worth the risk it involved.

One thing I knew: I would be glad enough to turn this job over to someone else—namely a city laundry. I sent Larry for the mail every day, hoping that there would be a message from my wandering sister. Housekeeping had me licked, I was ready to admit. This was too much.

One day, Larry came home from the post office looking very dignified. He was bearing a special delivery letter and was feeling important because he had been allowed to sign for it. It was from my sister and I opened it frantically, hoping to learn the date when I would be paroled. As I read the letter, my jaw dropped and Lynn asked anxiously:

"What's the matter, Daddy?"

I read them a paragraph from the letter:

". . . and when I got here, I found it's one of those no-animals, no-children-allowed apartments. So I'm afraid the arrangement I suggested is off. Of course, I can't find any place else for us to live up here. Maybe you can go to Florida and I only wish I could go down there with you . . ."

"Oh, boy!" whooped Larry. "We're going back to Florida!"

"Sand," the little one began to yell, dancing up and down. "All 'at sand in Floridy."

"Can we go, Daddy?" chorused Lynn.

"I'll see," I told them.

Later that day, a wire went off to our old friend Buttons which said:

"Will take one of your cabins for winter if you furnish snow shovel."

Buttons confirmed the arrangement a few days later and we appeared at the Union Station in Washington one afternoon in November. Our party included one beagle hound, two tomcats, three children, sixteen dolls, twenty-three pieces of assorted luggage, and, I suspected, some stowaways I didn't know about. I left the trunks and animals in the baggage room and hurried away before the baggage master could recognize Tonker and refuse us passage.

We burst into our car like a muffled explosion. The children took one quick look around and went into action. They had received a pre-departure lecture from me on how to behave on the train—including instructions on the operation of water fountains and wash basins. Also, I had given them a careful inspection for any signs of communicable diseases. This trip, I was determined, was going to be different.

Larry immediately spotted the inevitable sailor a couple of

[242]

seats behind us and made for him like a long-lost buddy. I handed out books to the girls, but as soon as the train pulled out they headed for the ladies' room. Left alone, I began to unwrap a book which my sister had sent me as a going-away present. When I found it was something called *The Mother's Encyclopedia,* I thrust it aside impatiently.

"At this point," I muttered, "I should be writing one."

A couple of seats ahead, there was a fat lady, wearing a black coat with a fur collar. My attention was attracted to her because there was a tiny blue turtle crawling on her collar and heading for her neck. Leaning forward, I saw on the turtle's back the inscription "LYNN." It was one of the girl's pets, which I had insisted on leaving behind.

I started to make a quick grab for the turtle, but I was afraid I would scare the daylights out of the lady and possibly cause unpleasant complications. Of course, I told myself, I could just let nature take its course, watch the fun, and pretend I'd never seen the beast before. Just then, I felt a tap on my shoulder. It was the porter.

"That little girl of yours got herself locked in, back in the ladies' room," he said, grinning, "But don't you worry, Cap'n, we'll get her out of there in a few minutes."

"You'll be sorry if you do," I said. "Couldn't you just leave her in there until bedtime?"

Suddenly, Lynn's turtle made contact with the fat lady and she shot up like a Roman candle. The turtle went down her back, under her dress, and she leaped into the aisle. She started to shake violently and the more she shook, the farther down the turtle went. The farther he went, the more she shook. For the weight she was carrying, she could certainly move around mighty spry. When she discovered that her frantic shakings

[243]

were accomplishing nothing, she streaked for the ladies' room. This, I knew, would be my undoing—because the minute that turtle saw light back there, Lynn was going to claim it as her own.

Maybe, I thought, eyeing the emergency cord speculatively, we could escape in the confusion if I pulled that thing. But then Larry sat down next to me.

"Nice sailor," he said. "Said he'd take me up to the club car after awhile."

"Humph," I replied.

Suddenly, I reached for my copy of *The Mother's Encyclopedia*. I was hoping that I would find a treatise on "What to Do with Children On a Train," or—better still—on "What to Do with Children."

"Boy," said Larry excitedly. "Just think, in the morning we'll be starting another winter in Florida."

"I can't wait," I said. "I just can't wait."